Barney Desai was born in Johannesburg in 1932. He is a former president of the South African Coloured People's Congress. He was elected Cape Town city councillor but was unable to take his seat because of a banning order which forbade him to be in a gathering of more than one person. He was gaoled during the 1960 'State of Emergency'. He escaped from South Africa in 1963 while on trial for breaking his banning order. He is now a barrister and lives in London with his wife and children.

Cardiff Marney was born in Cape Town in 1934. He was a full-time officer of the Union of Black Municipal Workers in Cape Town before he was banned and like Barney Desai he formerly held office in the South African Coloured People's Congress. He too was gaoled and spent 127 days in solitary confinement. Since 1964 he has lived with his family in exile in England.

THE KILLING OF THE IMAM

Barney Desai and Cardiff Marney
Foreword by Sir Dingle Foot QC

QUARTET BOOKS
LONDON   MELBOURNE   NEW YORK
in association with
THE BOWERDEAN PRESS

First published by Quartet Books Limited 1978
A member of the Namara Group
27 Goodge Street, London W1P 1FD

Copyright © 1978 by Barney Desai and Cardiff Marney
Foreword copyright © 1978 by Sir Dingle Foot QC

Extract from *117 Days* by Ruth First © 1965 by Ruth First, reprinted
by permission of the author and Penguin Books Limited

ISBN Hardcover 0 7043 2183 1
     Paperback 0 7043 3212 4

Typeset by Bedford Typesetters Limited
Printed in Great Britain by litho at The Anchor Press Ltd
and bound by Wm Brendon & Son Ltd
both of Tiptree, Essex

Against tyranny and injustice, for freedom and right, we dedicate this humble effort to the memory of the mighty heroes and the giants amongst men who have given up their lives so that South Africa may become a land of the free and the just.

Contents

Acknowledgements

We are grateful for the invaluable assistance afforded us by Lars Gunnar Ericksson, Canon John Collins and Zevia Desai

One of the strangest chapters in British history is the story of our relations with South Africa. The Boer War took place at the beginning of the century. The Conservative Party under the inspiration of Joseph Chamberlain were determined that Boer resistance should be crushed. The Liberals and Trades Unions – the Labour Party had not yet come fully into existence – took a somewhat different view. They sympathised with the Boers. When Boer women and children were herded into concentration camps Sir Henry Campbell-Bannerman denounced 'methods of barbarism'. Lloyd George was a pro-Boer. So indeed were many other left-wingers. It was not surprising that ten years later a Liberal Government should reach an agreement with the South African leaders on the future of the territory.

How different is the position today. South Africa is regarded almost by the whole world as the apotheosis of racial oppression. Writing in *The Times* Mr Bernard Levin, regarding the banning to political prisoners of all current world news, has referred to 'Mr Vorster's Mad, Mad Censors'. It would be difficult to find any influential politicians in this country who today would seek to exculpate the South African regime.

Nobody protested at the time. But in effect the Liberal British Government in 1910 handed over the lives and affairs of the black population to the white state.

It is sometimes forgotten that the subjugation met with desperate resistance. There was the Bambata rebellion in 1904 when four thousand Africans were slaughtered and the leader himself was beheaded. There have been many protests since then. In 1920 as many as twenty-one workers were killed in Port Elizabeth when they protested against the arrest of their trade union leaders. There have been other similar incidents – notably the massacre of Sharpville on 21st March, 1960. But the narrative does not end with occasional violent explosions. The South African Government has been at the utmost pains to suppress every form of political protest. The African National Congress and the Pan-Africanist Congress were suppressed in 1960. Thereafter, the Africans had only two forms of political expression. One was the Black Peoples Convention and the other the South African Students Organisation. No act of terrorist activity or terrorism has been alleged against either. Nevertheless the leaders of the two organisations – seven Africans and two Indians – were successfully prosecuted in 1976 under the Suppression of Terrorism Act. It was assumed that almost any form of political organisation by black people amounted to a conspiracy to overthrow the State.

In this book the authors tell the story of Abdulla Haron. He was the Muslim leader who became one of the principal victims of the regime. He endured many days of police interrogation. This may well have been because of his associations on his visits to the United Kingdom. He had been closely associated with Canon Collins and other exponents of African freedom. In the eyes of the regime this is unforgivable. He died as a result of manifold injuries. It is difficult, indeed almost impossible, to believe that this was all the result of an accidental fall. He died in September 1969. Since then attention has been concentrated on a very similar fatality – the death of Steve Biko. His experience in his last days cannot have been very different from that of Abdulla Haron.

Of course it is true that South Africa is not the only operative despotism of the modern world. There are many others, notably in the Soviet Union, Eastern Europe and South America. But there is this difference. The victims of Communist rule are not persecuted because of their race or colour but because they do not accept the dominance of a particular organisation. Jews are not persecuted in the Soviet Union because of their Hebraic beliefs but because they do not conform in every respect to Communist leadership. In South Africa there is no escape for those whose skins are black or brown.

The Rt Hon Sir Dingle Foot QC
February, 1978

Chapter One

The Man

In 1956, on the day that Muslims celebrate the birth of the prophet Muhammad, the congregation of the Al Jaamia mosque in the Cape Town suburb of Claremont appointed 32-year-old Hadji Abdulla Haron to be their 'Imam', that is, the leader of their obligatory prayers, interpreter of the Koran, counsellor of the young, adviser to the old, consoler of the anguished, mender of the broken in spirit. These are great responsibilities, but that is what the Imam is for – at least in Cape Town, where some 100,000 Muslims, commonly known as 'Cape Malays', are to be found. These Muslims form part of the $2\frac{1}{2}$ million racially mixed people which officialdom describes as 'Cape Coloured'.

The appointment of the young Abdulla Haron was a controversial decision. The older members of the congregation were opposed to him because of his youth and many felt that he was, in fact, too boyish in his ways. Some felt that he was not sufficiently learned in Islamic theology to carry out the responsibilities of an Imam, despite his good knowledge of Arabic and the three pilgrimages (Hadjes) he had undertaken to Mecca.

The importance of the Imam's appointment does not lie just in the breadth of his religious and spiritual responsibilities. He is also the symbol and custodian of a history and a tradition which he must treasure and pass on to succeeding generations. The lives of the Muslim community are suffused by their traditions

1

which, despite the prevailing racial hostility, have profoundly influenced the whole South African way of life. They expect of their leaders therefore that they should be faithful to a cultural heritage originating in the Orient.

The forebears of South Africa's mixed coloured community, the Khoisans, were the first Africans to come into contact with the early Portuguese explorers and then with the colonists who started their settlement in the Cape in 1652, when the Dutch East India Company built a victualling station despite the resistance of the aboriginal Khoisans. This resistance continued for many years but superior weaponry and organization won for the Dutch the area around what was to become Cape Town. At some time, the intruders presented to the natives a trunk of beads, mirrors and cloth to seal a bargain they had in fact already clinched with their guns. The ancient Khoisan custom of accepting gifts from strangers in exchange for the temporary use of their territory was naturally interpreted by the Dutch in their own cultural terms – as an outright purchase. In any case, it salved their capitalist consciences and gave white historians sufficient reason to claim the Cape as European property.

Because of Khoisan resistance both to the conquest of their country and, more especially, to the introduction of forced labour, the Dutch had to import slaves to meet their labour requirements. Perhaps half the slaves derived from east and west Africa and half from south-east Asia. Those from Malaysia and Indonesia practised the religion of Islam and managed, despite the hostile Christian surroundings and their isolation from their cultural roots, to cling to their faith. Thus it was that the white rulers, in their obsession with racial classification, came to create a special classification for Cape Malays – although the same white rulers studiously avoided calling themselves 'Cape Dutch'.

But the Dutch also exiled to the Cape the Indonesian prince, Sheikh Yusuf, who had risen in revolt against their rule in his native land. This prince was brought to the Cape with his family and a hundred or more of his followers and retainers. He is believed to be buried at Faurie, some twenty miles from Cape Town.

In view of his rank, the Dutch allowed the prince and his household and retainers a position of status and privilege. The Muslims of the Cape were permitted to found a memorial where thousands go and offer prayers for the long-dead Sheikh Yusuf. This memorial – an impressive tomb or 'kramat' – at Faurie, has been imitated in many other less impressive kramats in various parts of the Cape, marking the burial places of the followers of the Sheikh and some of his more illustrious descendants. (Interestingly, the modern Indonesian struggle against Dutch imperialism was launched from a similar memorial to the prince.) Clearly, it was the presence of these high-ranking exiles which accounted for the remarkable way in which a section of the Muslim slave population was able to cling to their religion and secure its continued observance amongst the Cape Coloureds.

Relatively little miscegenation occurred between Khoisans and Europeans, and the slaves operated as a consanguineous link. It was in their ranks that considerable miscegenation with the aboriginals occurred – some Khoisans had in fact become enslaved themselves; slaves ran away to join Khoisan tribes; and half the slaves were in any case of African origin. The slaves, irrespective of religion, absorbed every racial strain existing in the Cape and were eventually themselves absorbed, to become racially indistinguishable from what became known as Cape Coloureds by the British.

A later element was added to the Muslim community by the introduction under the British rule of semi-slave 'indentured labour' from India. Some of these Indian semi-slaves were followers of Islam and those who found their way to the Cape were received into the embrace of the Muslims and further enriched the religious and social life of the community. These Indians also laid great emphasis upon the oriental aspect of the cultural life of the Muslim faith, to which they had clung through thick and thin.

This was the background against which the elders of Haron's congregation began somewhat anxiously to try to reach a decision.

Haron was a dapper little man who wore his black fez perched at altogether too-fashionable an angle upon a controversially clean-shaven head. Many thought that such a person was not quite suitable to be an Imam. Would he command respect? Could he temper his irrepressible humour and ready laughter? (Religious leaders are supposed to be serious people!) Above all, the older members of the congregation, which numbered in all

3

about 2000, were not quite sure whether, theologically speaking, his weekly evening out at the cinema might not be more profitably spent in prayer and pious meditation.

Haron was a devotee of rugby and had played for the Watsonians Rugby Club. But that was understandable – the game was an obsession with every Muslim. Although religious considerations naturally counted most, had Haron been a great rugby player he might well have won instant and universal support from his congregation. However, he could only manage a place in the second team, where his most notable attribute was found to be his piety. As a result there was much humming and hawing about his candidature for the Imamship.

Abdulla Haron was noted for his simplicity, modesty and piety. He was known as a man of the people, and the working people in particular responded to his clear qualities of leadership. He was their choice and, because the Imam is appointed by election, he won. Abdulla Haron's personality remained un-altered but he developed and grew in office. He retained his youthful demeanour despite the weight of responsibility and the passage of the years. He continued to work at his father's business, a small grocery shop, and to earn his keep there. Upon his appointment he insisted that he could both earn his own living and perform his duties at the mosque. As a matter of principle he would refuse the customary sealed envelope containing some undisclosed fee for the baptism of the newly born, the solemnization of marriage or the leading of the prayers for the dead. It was widely believed that he should have had a proper stipend, as the grocery shop hardly produced enough income for the two families it had to support – his own and that of his father. His firm stand on principle therefore attracted great admiration. The new Imam naturally spent much time in prayer and meditation, but he and his wife still went regularly to the cinema as they always had. His taste in films was no different from that of the majority of his congregation – like them he loved the James Bond movies, relishing no less than they did the escapist fantasies without which their daily lives would have been that much duller. One evening he went to see *Judgement at Nuremberg*, about the trial for war crimes of the Nazi leaders. The film had a deep effect upon him. He began to think about political events in his own country – could such a trial ever take

4

place in South Africa? His interest in future developments began to intensify.

Abdulla Haron's mother had died when he was barely two months old, leaving a family of two boys and three girls. His father had married again and this second marriage brought an increase of seven to the family – one step-brother and six step-sisters. For this reason Haron was entrusted to the care of his aunt Miriam who brought him up. She was a very indulgent foster-mother in many ways, but she showed special concern for his religious and spiritual education. On three occasions, first when he was eight, then at fourteen and again in his early twenties, she took him on a pilgrimage to Mecca at her own expense. This was an enormous undertaking and reflected the considerable financial sacrifice that she was willing to make on Haron's behalf. In all, they spent some six years in Egypt and Saudi Arabia, thus more than fulfilling the religious obligation imposed upon every Muslim to undertake the pilgrimage to Mecca at least once in a lifetime. Millions of Muslims from all parts of the world gather in Mecca, travelling on foot, by donkey, bus, ship or aeroplane, to perform their prayers in the vicinity of the Kaaba (the holiest of the shrines of Islam). Such pilgrims are called 'Al Hadj' or 'Hadji', and great religious as well as social prestige is accorded them.

The pilgrimages to Mecca served Abdulla Haron well. He became fluent in Arabic and by the age of fourteen could recite faultlessly every verse of the Koran by heart. This feat, though not uncommon throughout the Islamic world, is nevertheless one that requires great resources of intellect and self-discipline, especially in the young. He studied Islamic theology as the pupil of a number of leading Imams and Sheikhs, and in particular he sat at the feet of the greatly venerated Sheikh Ismail – one of the foremost religious leaders of the Cape community. This was how he acquired the learning necessary to pronounce authoritatively upon the many theological problems of Islam. He learned all that there was to know of the birth of Islam fourteen hundred years ago; of the ethos and culture that developed as a result; of the wisdom and beauty of the Koranic verses and of the schisms which developed among the Holy Prophet's successors. But although through this learning Haron was introduced to the whole spectrum of Islamic wisdom, there remained one area

5

upon which his scholarly and religious teachers failed to touch. Neither publicly nor privately were any answers forthcoming on the application of the Islamic creed to the problems of contemporary South African society. His teachers, for all their learning, left Abdulla Haron in a political limbo.

The secular State may have had an interest in encouraging an 'other-worldly' approach to religious matters, but it had been borne in on Haron very early in his studies that Islam was not an other-worldly religion. This was clear in the teaching of the prophet Muhammad himself and in the quotations or proverbs to be found displayed in the mosques. In a famous Cape Town mosque were tapestries bearing the words:

'Enthusiasm is the vehicle of my life'
'Contemplation of Allah is my compassion'
'Faith is the source of my power'
'Sorrow is my friend'
'Knowledge is my weapon'
'Truth is my salvation'
'Worship is my habit'
'Love of all men is the core of my belief'

So it was Haron's very knowledge of Islam that led early on to his first hesitant and inchoate interest in the social and political affairs of his people.

In 1950 Abdulla Haron married Galiema Sadan. He was in fact engaged to someone else at the time – someone chosen by his foster-mother. This fact was known to Galiema when he first set out to court her, and his attentions were not particularly welcome as a result. Moreover, at that time he was passing through a phase which expressed itself in the most bizarre taste in clothing. The Americans had just startled the world with their 'zoot suits'. Haron took to wearing two-toned white and black patent-leather shoes, lurid bow-ties and the widest possible flared trousers. In fact, everything he wore shrieked of colour – far in excess of anything that could have been attributed simply to the traditional oriental love of splendour! Galiema Sadan tried every possible means to put him off but without success. They had known each other at school – a fact which Haron was quite ready to exploit to the full – and in the end his persistence triumphed. In time he learned to restrain his colour sense, but his persistence increased and became one of his most notable character traits.

The beginnings of their marriage were mean and poor. Their first home was a tiny room with an attached kitchen on two small plots of land that Abdulla's aunt had given him. It was situated in a relatively undeveloped area of dairy farms, open fields and unmade roads. Gradually, more rooms were added as and when they could afford to buy materials and when relatives and friends – many of whom were building workers of some skill – could be coaxed into helping at weekends. This sort of mutual help was known as 'kanala jobs' ('please jobs'), as no payment was involved. The Cape Coloureds are the oldest section of the South African working-class and not surprisingly possess a considerable fund of skills. This is nowhere more apparent than in the building industry which they developed and which produced the beautiful old Dutch-gabled houses of the Cape.

While Abdulla tended the grocery shop Galiema worked at her sewing machine, producing the fine ladies' garments which have given the Muslims such a richly deserved reputation for dress-making and tailoring. It was the income derived from this labour which kept the family solvent. Galiema became the family banker, very often having to make good the Imam's rash promises of help to others who were in difficulty. Abdulla Haron had a weakness for helping others – something he in any case considered himself obligated by his religion to do. This some-times caused domestic problems. Fortunately his wife was a very efficient housewife and also a supremely capable mother to their three children. Their eldest, Shamela, was born at the end of 1950; Mohammed, their one son, was born in 1957; Fatima was born in 1963.

As the family grew, so did the house so that by 1966 they had an attractive three-bedroom home with a long porch and large windows. Near by, flowed that lovely little stream known as the Kromboom River which meanders through the lower reaches of the suburbs of Claremont, bordering the approaches to the Cape Flats. From his home it had been just a short walk to a rustic foot-bridge over the stream, beyond which he could stroll about on the large open spaces on which rugby, soccer and cricket were often played. Things were looking good, at least on the surface, when tragedy intervened in the shape of the dreaded race laws.

As the area in which the Harons lived became relatively developed, so it became more desirable to the whites. First option to purchase their home, which was in an area now declared 'for white occupation', belonged to that agency of the State known as the Group Areas Board. The Board chose to exercise its option, so the Harons were obliged to move to an area set aside for 'coloured occupation'. Fortunately, by this time the Haron family finances had considerably improved so Haron purchased the usual fifty by one hundred foot plot of land in the best situation he could find in the 'Coloured Group Area'.

The Cape Flats is the area to which the vast majority of the black people of the Cape Peninsula were driven by the policies of the State. It is an area between the mountain chain which forms the Cape Peninsula and the coastal hills where the main mass of the African continent begins. Stretching from Table Bay in the north to False Bay in the south, it was, in distant geological time, part of the sea-bed; and it retains the character of low-lying, relatively infertile swathe of white sand on which the dry south-east gales of summer and the rain-bearing north-westers of winter will often produce, in season, shifting sand-dunes or floods. Before the arrival of the Europeans the area had been covered with grass as far as the eye could see and the Khoisans used it for winter grazing for their great herds of cattle and sheep. Overworked by the Europeans, who also introduced to the area the horrible stunted 'Port Jackson' tree which flourishes and destroys grazing land, the sands have been loosened and the conditions are often very unpleasant. The worst parts have been set aside for occupation by black people, but the Harons were fortunate to acquire land in a better part.

With a loan from a relative to supplement his own capital and with the willing hands of the skilled workers of his congregation, he built a house opposite a playing field. The situation could not compare with that of his previous home, but the new house opposite the rugby ground was not too badly situated and gave him a grandstand view of the game he loved. Indeed, Haron had a balcony built onto the house to make it even better. But even this did not stop him from making his way into the ground itself where he could participate in the cheering, cursing and caterwauling along with the crowds.

The Harons were a closely knit family. Throughout the twenty years of his marriage, Abdulla Haron always seemed to be courting his wife. He was that kind of man. For his children he sought education, almost to the point of desperation. This may have been prompted by his conviction that his own secular education had been inadequate. Because of his poverty, deliberate neglect by the racialist State, and the emphasis placed by his aunt upon his religious education, it had been limited to primary schooling only. Of course, he saw to it that his own children were thoroughly educated in the ways and rules of Islam; but he felt deeply that they must have a proper secular education as well. He longed for them to qualify in professions where they could be of service to others and at the same time make their way in the world. As a Cape Malay he was, furthermore, particularly aware of the estrangement suffered by Muslims in a strongly Calvinistic Christian society. The discrimination to which his people were exposed was not only racial but religious as well. Because the education of Cape Coloureds had for many years been under the control of the Christian church, restrictions and difficulties had always attended the education of Muslim children. As a result, for all the magnificent craftsmanship which they displayed in the building and clothing industries, and despite their mastery of the domestic arts, they had tended to underrate the importance of academic education. The special schools they had managed to establish were insufficient and inadequate, owing to a severe shortage of money. But a new spirit of awareness was abroad, and it was to this new spirit that Haron was drawn. He was filled with a keen desire to stimulate and support the aspirations of his people.

For this reason he was enormously pleased when his elder daughter completed her high school education. She wanted to become a radiographer, so in 1968, because of the limitations on her potential imposed in South Africa by apartheid, he sent her overseas. He was able to afford to send her on the highly prized hadj to Mecca, after which she could continue to London where he had arranged for friends to assist her with gaining admission to a training hospital. Just as he had done his own first hadj at the age of eight, so he had seen to it that his son benefited from the experience at the same age. But in addition Haron ensured that the boy's secular education was not neglected as his had been.

It did not escape his notice that the demands for secular State schools, removed from the Church's control, came most often from young graduate teachers who were often condemned either as too political or as atheists. It was one such graduate, a Christian and one of the country's leading rugby players, who joined his rugby club as a deliberate act of protest against the discrimination practised against the Muslims, thereby bringing considerable prestige to the club. Such discrimination was widespread in the field of sport though non-existent in the political life of the community where Muslims in fact played a considerable part. There were clubs which refused admission to Muslims, so promoting the notion of 'Christian Clubs' and 'Muslim Clubs'. Examples, like that of the rugby player, which crossed the religious divide gave Haron much food for thought.

Historically there had been easy relations between the different religious groups but the white policy of 'divide and rule' had done all in its power to create animus and division. Although leaders of the Cape Coloured community fought hard to combat this between 1930 and 1940, the grounds for mutual distrust had been laid long before. The descendants of the original Khoisans were reviled as 'bushmen' and 'hottentots', while those descended from the imported slave population were encouraged by the whites to segregate themselves from these Africans, even though the blood of the two strains was deeply intermingled within the community. Great prestige attached to proof of European descent or to any foreign origins – anything was preferable to African ancestry. Those best placed to claim foreign origin (and thus to dissociate themselves from any suggestion of Khoisan descent) were the Muslims and those from St Helena and Mauritius. This they were of course encouraged to do; at the same time, Christians were encouraged to resent Muslims, and so the vicious circle was drawn.

Religious discrimination was a matter of deep concern to Abdulla Haron. Not only did it make for a community divided against itself, but it led many of the educated and progressive

10

elements in the community to cut themselves off from their religious background altogether. Only by doing so did they feel able to function effectively in the political and cultural fields. Haron concluded from this that it was vitally necessary to make his religious teaching socially relevant so that thrusting, progressive, educated young Muslims would not leave the Islamic fold.

It was a momentous time. The struggle had begun – against apartheid, against inferior schooling, against Group Areas oppression – and for non-racialism. Racial and religious discrimination in sport and social matters was being countered and slowly overcome. It was hardly surprising that Abdulla Haron should seek to extend his horizons beyond the limits of his strict religious responsibilities.

Not that he saw any contradiction between his religion and his concern for principles such as social justice and education. His knowledge of Islam taught him that the prophet Muhammad was an unlettered man who had nevertheless enjoined his followers, both men and women, to seek knowledge 'even if you have to go to China for it'. The proverbs of Islam are suffused with this emphasis upon knowledge. But the racialist State in which Haron lived was actively engaged in an effort to down-grade the education available to his people by extending apartheid, and thus inferior education, to university level. So strong was the hostility that this policy aroused, that in 1959 an all but successful attempt at arson was made upon the segregated and inferior 'University College of the West Cape' which had been specially created for Cape Coloureds. At every point, therefore, it seemed that religious, personal and social concerns crossed and inter-connected. It followed that he could not remain indifferent to the implications the implementation of the Group Areas laws would have for his mosque, for the homes of his congregation, and for human suffering at large.

So it became apparent that even if Abdulla Haron had wanted to leave politics alone, politics was not going to leave him alone. There was in any case a strong tradition of Muslim participation in the political life of the community. The young Imam was prepared, perhaps more than his predecessors had been, to listen to the ideas of the younger members of his congregation.

11

He became the medium through which the new spirit of the age was filtered to his people. So, gradually, as his mind and interests broadened, his political education took shape. From about 1960 onwards he began to take a positive interest in developments within the organizations working towards liberation.

Chapter Two

A Priest for the Times

The appointment of Abdulla Haron to the Imamship did not immediately find favour with some of the educated younger members of the congregation who had opposed his nomination on the grounds that they wanted an 'older, more experienced leader'. Very soon, however, these same younger members became his staunchest and most devoted supporters and students. 'In fact', we are told, 'he attracted many young members from the other mosques and he united the local Muslims into an active and cohesive community.' On his appointment he immediately founded a 'Madressa' (a religious school for the young) and taught them Arabic so that they might approach the Koran with understanding rather than simply learning long passages off by heart to repeat parrot-fashion without any trace of comprehension. Haron always maintained that his young scholars were not robots but people who needed to understand the message so that they might be sustained by it. He freely admitted that many Muslims, who were thoroughly versed in the teaching of Islam, were often deeply perplexed, how to relate their faith to contemporary issues. Haron's own youthfulness made him deeply sympathetic to this very perplexity and he was willing to learn from those among his congregation whose secular education had developed their political awareness.

The greatest threat facing the whole black population, and

the Cape Coloureds in particular, was the Group Areas Act. The Act, which became law in 1950, threatened the blacks with mass removals. Homes, mosques, churches, schools, businesses and even recreation facilities were, under the terms of this law, to be moved into the appropriate 'Bantu', 'Coloured', 'Malay' or 'Indian' group areas, according to the racial classification of the occupier or user. Although the law applied throughout the country, the Cape Peninsula had a peculiar history which left many blacks in occupation of the old areas near the city centre. Subsequent movement to the suburbs had proceeded in leap-frog fashion, with the blacks moving out beyond a white settlement, then the whites leaping over a black locality to some desirable area further out, and so on. During the centuries there had also arisen groupings of little cottages for working men which served local labour needs; a cluster of houses here, a street there, a few blocks elsewhere – perhaps bordering a commercial area or the outlying dairy farms which were themselves being slowly squeezed out as population and industry encroached upon available land. The demographic map was therefore like a patchwork quilt. In the Cape Peninsula there were more 'Mixed' areas and 'racial pockets' than in any other part of the country.

Over a long period of time the authorities had adopted a complex series of administrative devices to separate whites and blacks: a street leading from one area to another might be blocked and a house or two built to seal off the route; a necessary through-road elsewhere would not be built, but housing would be established to break the communication; a re-development would be embarked upon which would require the demolition of 'black spots'. The chief device was to build necessary housing schemes only in areas which were strictly zoned on racial lines, and it was for this purpose that the area of the Cape Flats was chosen. Under the terms of the Group Areas Act, however, this gradual and pragmatic approach was done away with. Soon the bureaucrats of the State, sitting in the security of their offices, smug in the knowledge that their own homes and properties would not be touched and oblivious to the suffering produced by their decisions, were radically redrafting the racial boundary lines – here a buffer zone, there a railway line and in some other place perhaps a river or a road. Move the

14

Indians ten miles away from this established business area; shift this coloured community to the sandy wastes; but consolidate these white suburbs into a large region of desirable land.

Inquiries into the proposals were formally conducted by a Group Areas Board. Affected people could submit petitions and pathetic memoranda and their lawyers could wail about 'cruelty' and 'injustice', 'robbery' and 'inhumanity' – some even talked of 'genocide' – but nobody paid the slightest attention. The so-called inquiries were in practice no more than echo chambers. The voices of the plaintiffs rose to a crescendo and then gradually died away.

Fearing reprisals if they disobeyed, most people moved where they were instructed. Some fought unsuccessful rear-guard actions in the courts, but many more emigrated – sold up and left their homes and ancestral homeland for ever. As they left, new waves of European immigrants moved in, sometimes right into the very houses from which the heirs of the Khoisans had just been driven.

The Muslims especially were filled with anguish at the effects of the Group Areas Act. Not only their homes but their places of worship, the mosques, were frequently to be found in the older parts of the city. Like so many others, Abdulla Haron found himself under threat of expulsion from his home but, worse still, from his mosque also. This led him to make a brave decision. What happened to his home was one thing, but the fate of the mosque was another matter entirely, and called in question his spiritual as well as his temporal responsibilities. At a gathering of the Muslim Judicial Council – a body which had been established to care for the joint and common religious concerns of all mosques and their congregations – he declared that, in accordance with Koranic law 'the precincts of the mosque are inviolable and the building sacred forever. No mosque can be sold or destroyed.'

This declaration created a sensation. It amounted to an assertion that for the State to seize the mosques was to be regarded as the declaration of a Holy War. The Imam's stand won the backing of the community and as the degree of support for it became clear, for once the State capitulated. The mosques, but not of course the homes of the Muslims, were to be exempted from the Group Areas Act.

By the third year of his Imamship, Haron had built up a very active congregation. Fêtes and picnics became a regular feature of the life of the congregation, and in this way funds were raised to help the poor. Women's work and study circles were established, and youth study groups flourished. A library of religious works was created in the mosque by the leading study group, known as the Ibadurahman Study Group, and it came to be generally agreed that proselytizing work amongst black African migrant labourers was necessary. These men were penned in prison-like compounds and were generally despised. Haron was determined that the word of Islam should be brought to them also. Managing in one way or another to circumvent the various bureaucratic restrictions placed in his path, he set out to seek converts and, to his astonishment, he found many eager to listen to his message. These new converts in turn served to stimulate his political interest. Here, among the most oppressed pass-bearing people, he discovered an impatience for and a confidence in national liberation such as he had not previously encountered. For the first time, he came across an organization called the Pan-Africanist Congress which was then engaged in preparing yet another assault on the tyrannical 'pass laws'.

Haron was struck by the contrast between the impatient activism which prevailed in the camps of the migrant labourers and the talkative theorizing of certain young members of his own congregation who had links with another organization known as the Unity Movement.

He sought guidance from two sources. First, of course, he scoured the Holy Koran until he found what he was looking for. 'The brotherhood of man' became a regular theme for the talks and study groups which Haron had made a feature of the life of the mosque. Secondly, he began to seek out informed and experienced people with whom he could discuss the political problems that faced them. There were members of the Unity Movement within his own congregation and from them he learned a good deal of history. But for information about the political events taking place elsewhere he had to find and approach others. In this way he came to establish close friendship with a certain Mujaheed who was connected with an organization known as the Coloured People's Congress (CPC),

Mujaheed became the contact through which Haron met members of the African National Congress, the South African Indian Congress and various other parties which together constituted what became known as the 'Congress Alliance'. These were the parties that had been in the forefront of the political struggle for some years. Haron was interested to discover that their members were not the frightening fanatics sometimes depicted in the newspapers, but were reasonable and intelligent men with families they loved and cherished just like himself. As a result his friendships with politically active people grew in number and in strength.

Haron found himself looking more and more to the Koran and to the trials and tribulations of the prophet Muhammad to shed light on the many political problems with which, increasingly, he was faced. He looked also for reassurance that Holy Writ approved his decision to discuss these problems with his congregation and with his fellow Muslims both in sermons and privately.

He shared his doubts and uncertainties on the subject with 'Abraham', a fellow Muslim. 'I know,' said Haron, 'that the power of prayer can move mountains. We must ask the people to have faith. If, on a chosen day, we ask all the people to go down on their knees in prayer, Allah will surely work a change of heart on the white people. We could will such a change of heart, I'm sure of it.'

'Ah, if only such things could be,' replied Abraham. 'You mention a chosen day? We had such a day once in this country, you know, but it led only to disaster.' And he told Haron the following story:

'After the Khoisans were overrun by the Europeans, the Xhosa people became the foremost defenders of the country. They fought many wars against the white man but they never achieved victory. Every day the Xhosa became weaker and more desperate, so terrible was their suffering. One day, a young girl named Nonquase came to the elders of the tribe and said that she was a prophet and had had a dream in which she saw visions of great victories for her people. That year, said the girl, the Xhosa were not to plant any crops; they were to kill all their cattle and eat their fill; there should be nothing left to eat. Then, on a certain day, the sun would rise half-way up the sky and

17

then stop there. Suddenly, crops and cattle in abundance would rise out of the ground and there would be eating and dancing and rejoicing such as in the days of old. With the crops and cattle would also rise out of the ground all the mighty warriors and heroes of old who would then drive the white man into the sea. Oh, how the Xhosa people prayed and willed that these things should happen. But when the great day came, they starved. Thousands died. And the white man is still here.'

'But,' protested Haron, 'they did all the wrong things. And, anyway, they weren't Muslims in the first place.'

'Neither are all the black people in the country today,' answered Abraham. 'Besides, you know very well that the prophet Muhammad led his people to war. The Muslims had to fight many wars before they were victorious. They didn't just kneel down and pray for salvation.'

Haron thought long and hard about this. The prospect of bloodshed did not appeal to him. In the end he concluded that although prayer could achieve great things, on its own praying was insufficient. So he continued to pray and to agonize, until quite suddenly his mind was made up for him by the events that occurred on and following 21 March 1960.

All black Africans in South Africa (that is, people who are not classified under the racial laws as 'white', 'Indian' or 'Coloured') are required to have in their possession at all times a document known as a 'pass'. In the days of slavery a pass had been simply a letter authorizing the slave to be away from the premises of his owner. But the purpose of the modern pass is racial. It concerns control of ostensibly free labour and is a complex document permitting continuous harassment by the police and other authorities. Many struggles had been waged against the pass laws and, on 21 March 1960, the Pan Africanist Congress launched another such struggle. The members of the Congress declared that they would carry a pass no longer and, together with many thousands of people, presented themselves for arrest at police stations all over the country in a display of passive resistance. Despite the passivity of the crowds the reaction of the police was very violent. Sixty-nine people were shot dead and many more injured at the town of Sharpville in the Transvaal Province. This led to demonstrations, riots, strikes and general disorder, which caused the government to call out the army. They declared a state of emergency, out-lawed the Pan-Africanist Congress and the African National Congress, and jailed some 20,000 people who were known for their political activities. The disorder was greatest in the Cape, and the reaction of the army was to surround and seal off the African residential areas. Great suffering was caused and food shortages verging upon starvation occurred.

Abdulla Haron, deeply affected by these events and by the situation that developed as a result, took part in a spontaneous movement which developed to send supplies of food into the locations and the townships. He organized bread-collections and obtained supplies of food from small shop-keepers and even from poor families who had scarcely enough themselves. He found ways to run the gauntlet of army patrols to ensure that this food reached the sufferers, and it was in this way that he first came to the attention of the political police.

Soon after the end of the state of emergency, Haron was asked to serve on a fund-raising committee which was estab-lished in order to provide money for the legal defence of victims of the political police. The defendants, opponents of apartheid, were more often than not extremely poor workers who could not themselves afford lawyers to represent them in court. Generally, too, their families were left destitute by the inevitable imprison-ment which followed because the State made no provision for them.

Shortly afterwards, Haron found himself engaged in another activity which he regarded as equally important and which he found just as exciting. He had already made some converts to Islam in the black African population from the townships of Langa, Nyanga and Guguleta on the outskirts of Cape Town. As a result of the brutality of the State during the state of emergency, he now found an increasingly widespread expression of disgust with Christianity among these people and in par-ticular among the younger members of the Pan-Africanist Congress. Many were drawn to Islam and some became con-verts. Haron made himself the foremost spokesman amongst Muslims on the subject of missionary work and he undertook a large area of responsibility for it. Such activity had no precedent in South African history, and remains one of Haron's most widely remembered achievements.

19

But Abdulla Haron was not to be permitted to depart from the political field for the safer and greener pastures of missionary endeavour. South Africa was in the process of leaving the (British) Commonwealth and a new republican constitution was promulgated, to take effect on 31 May 1961. But as the black African majority were in no way consulted and were, on the contary, to have their rightlessness re-affirmed in the new arrangements, protests, demonstrations and conferences were once more taking place in another upsurge of political activity. A general strike, which was to last three days, was called and Haron found himself involved. On this occasion the involvement went even further than the charitable work he had done during the state of emergency. He actually supported the strike from the mimbar (pulpit) of his mosque, by appealing to his congregation to adopt the traditional Islamic mode of support by fasting for the three days of the strike. He also gave direct assistance to the work of the Coloured People's Congress (CPC), which was working for the strike, by arranging 'safe houses' where 'agitators' who were being hunted by the political police could hide.

This was a period of intense political activity for Haron. He became involved in an important conference (the Coloured Convention) which was taking place at the time. Although the conference was outlawed by the government it continued to meet clandestinely and some of its meetings were held in Haron's own home. He began to lend his support to the Coloured People's Congress although he did not actually become a member. As a religious leader he was able to campaign for candidates of the CPC in local council elections and against 'collaborators' (black supporters of white supremacist parties). Slowly his religious and political concerns began to come together in the struggle for liberation, and Haron learned to accept the element of personal danger with which this was inevitably attended.

By now he was no longer an impoverished shopkeeper. He had been forced to sell his shop and had in fact been unemployed for almost a year when by good fortune he obtained a position as sales representative for a large chocolate company at an attractive salary. The pressure of this work did not however prevent him from accepting the position of 'honorary editor' of

Muslim News – the only Muslim newspaper in the country. This gave him a political perspective on events far superior to that of any other member of the Islamic clergy and also helped him to consolidate the friendships he had established with leading members of the CPC.

The political situation now began to deteriorate. One after another, his new political friends started to disappear. First 'Gamat' (otherwise known as Teddy), an office-holder in the CPC and a councillor of the City of Cape Town, was imprisoned on Robben Island on grounds of incitement and sabotage. Then his successor on the City Council, Mujaheed, was prevented by the Security Police from taking his seat and, along with another official of the CPC, was forced to flee the country. Just before the promulgation of the 90-day law (April 1963) which provided for the detention in solitary confinement of all opponents of apartheid, Haron's friend Abraham was obliged to flee the country with the police on his tail. Many others were detained in solitary confinement or forced to leave the country.

Haron began to feel more and more isolated. The discovery that police informers had been placed in his congregation made him especially cautious. He began to weigh carefully the tone of any political pronouncements he made, though his struggle against poverty and oppression remained as passionate as ever. Conspicuously outstanding were the needs of families of political detainees. The State appeared to take special relish in persecuting them so as to exert pressure on their captive. The present dangerous times and the meagre resources available did not permit much to be done for these unfortunate people, but as much as could be was done.

By 1965 the government had achieved complete victory over such organized resistance as the black people could offer. Satisfied that its sophisticated terror machine was in good working order it felt able to relax a little and permit those who wished to exercise their social consciences to do so within the context of the existing political structure – in other words, apartheid. This meagre opportunity was seized upon by Haron who began to find a focus for his energies once more, and to speak about the many matters of general concern which affected them all. His Friday sermons became major events, keenly anticipated and widely discussed afterwards. There was a feeling among some members of the Muslim Judicial Council that Abdulla Haron's preoccupation with politics was unhealthy, but this feeling was not shared by young Muslims to whom he had become an idol. His name was by now widely known throughout Muslim circles in South Africa.

Towards the end of 1965 Haron became aware that the CPC was in fact still functioning – albeit underground. It was not formally outlawed as an organization but, in spite of this, a number of its members were suddenly arrested. Haron's previous lack of official connection with the organization now began to pay off. Gamat emerged from his terrible ordeal on Robben Island. Although under house arrest and suffering daily harassment from the police, Gamat renewed his political activities and enlisted Haron's support. For the first time Haron became deeply involved in the CPC as a member, once more assisting with fund-raising for the party.

This marked a new stage in his political development. He had placed the immense personal prestige that he had accumulated over the last few years at the disposal of the CPC. It also marked the moment when a certain Major Genis of the political police in the Cape decided that Abdulla Haron was a 'security risk'.

A few months later, the political police had even greater cause for concern. The CPC broke off its association with the Congress Alliance, dissolved itself, and called upon its members to join the Pan-Africanist Congress, following an invitation to the CPC to that effect. The consequences of this were that at that time – March 1966 – Abdulla Haron's political career entered its most hazardous phase to date. He was now a member of a party dedicated to the overthrow of apartheid by all means at its disposal, including violence.

Chapter Three

Political Pilgrimage

Late in 1966 Abdulla Haron felt that the time was right for another hadj. He badly needed some respite from the stifling political climate of South Africa. He needed a complete change and an opportunity for social, political and spiritual renewal. He was excited at the prospect of meeting some of the friends who had been forced into exile, and he informed Gamat of his plan to go to Mecca with Galiema. This information was passed on to Mujaheed who had escaped from South Africa in 1963 and was now in England with Abraham and others, working for the PAC. So when the Imam and his wife left for his fourth hadj in December, a rendezvous with Abraham in Mecca had already been arranged.

Haron loved Mecca. It revitalized him spiritually and brought back powerful memories of his childhood and youth. It was also a rest from the cares and worries of his everyday life. It was to be enjoyed as a holiday, even if the underlying purpose was a serious one. The city can become oppressively hot but this never disturbed him. As was the custom he would merely return to his room and sleep. His room was in an apartment building which, like hundreds of others, clusters around the Kaaba, like so many bunches of dates on a fruitful palmtree. It was here, one hot morning as he was resting, that he was awakened by the stentorian tones of Abraham bellowing outside his window. Soon they were locked in an emotional embrace, hugging and

23

kissing each other in Arab fashion. Haron was overwhelmed with joy to see his squat friend again. This was Abraham who had made such a dramatic escape from South Africa in 1963, Abraham the shopkeeper and loyal friend who had done so much to influence his own political stance. They had much to tell each other.

'I'm getting up now, Galiema,' said Haron. 'I'm done with sleeping. Don't expect to see much of me from now on.' Galiema knew that protest was useless. The men wanted to talk their 'men's business' and, like most women of her faith, she accepted that it was better that women keep out.

They had much to discuss. Haron was anxious to hear about all his old friends, Mujaheed and the others. Abraham was able to reassure him that they were all well and greatly looking forward to seeing him. So, between obligatory prayers and an afternoon nap they proceeded to exhaust personal matters, the latest gossip and tit-bits of news from home and abroad. Evening found them sitting in one of the roof-top cafés for which Mecca is famous, sipping the syrupy Turkish coffee, kahwa, and green tea. With a pitch-black night sky and stars so brilliant and seemingly so close it was almost as if a raised hand might pluck them from the sky, the two South Africans began to speak of the things closest to their hearts.

Abraham wanted to know how Gamat had survived his ordeal on Robben Island. 'We've been trying to persuade him of the need for his presence in Lesotho to join the PAC committee there. Have you any idea what the hold-up is?'

Haron replied that the experience had taken a terrible toll on Gamat's health. 'He's been fixed up with a little shop of his own and manages to make a living – but don't ask too much of him at this stage. I don't have to tell you that he's one of the people the Special Branch keep a very close watch on.'

Abraham listened to Haron with special intentness and pleasure. He recalled that this was the only Imam in his personal experience whose lessons from the mimbar had helped him to relate his religious life to his social existence. In many ways, each had contributed to the other's growth, approaching from different positions – the one religious, the other political – to establish a common ground. In the three and a half years since they had last seen each other, Abdulla Haron had de-

24

veloped enormously. And now he was in Mecca for political purposes. This was wonderful, Abraham mused to himself.

They talked about the PAC. For both of them the merger had presented some problems, including the loss of some comrades and friends, but both were convinced that it had been the right thing to do. Abraham mentioned a document that had been published which explained the rationale behind the merger, adding that they had not been able to infiltrate copies into South Africa on the scale which they regarded as necessary. However, he had some spare copies for Haron and others in South Africa to look at, something Haron promised to do.

For his part, Haron had some searching questions to put to Abraham about reports that had reached him of waste and extravagance amongst the exiles, especially of 'Hilton Hotel revolutionaries'. 'Don't you realize,' he asked Abraham, 'the propaganda value that the government derives from all this? One of your own close comrades who was in the same branch of the CPC as you has become a prominent journalist and is actually himself writing such reports! What's going on with you people, hey?' Abraham was quick to point out in return that the journalist in question had not only left the party but had now gone over to the other side, but he did concede that, nevertheless, there was some truth in what he had written. Against that though, the fact remained that many exiles lived in great poverty, many were in refugee camps, and the guerillas themselves endured great hardships.

Having reassured the Imam on this point, Abraham was able to put to him the request that he had been asked to make: that Haron should delay his return to South Africa and instead proceed, first to Cairo for discussions with the representatives of the Pan-Africanist Congress, and then to London. 'We are most insistent that if it is at all possible you should come to London to discuss a matter of some importance,' emphasized Abraham.

Haron was delighted and agreed with alacrity. Abraham was authorized to go ahead and arrange the tickets for Galiema and the Imam. 'Meanwhile,' said Haron, 'here is what we must do. Firstly, you know that the World Islamic Council is meeting here. The individual members come from all over the world. Our job is to approach them and explain the situation in South

Africa and then ask them to talk to their governments about taking action to help our struggle. This is the most important job. We have three weeks and we can do it.

'Secondly, we must produce a leaflet for the South Africans who are here. You know they come from all over the country and some of the silly fools come and stare at the Kaaba. We have to inform them through a leaflet and by talking to them personally where their duty as Muslims lies. We must remind them of their oppressed countrymen, and ask them to say a prayer for the victims of apartheid and for their families, and for the struggle. We must also call upon them to fight apartheid when they return home. That is their duty as Muslims! Well? Will you help me? Will you do it?' Haron's tone was urgent and demanding.

'Of course! For goodness' sake!' replied the astonished Abraham. He hesitated, peering awkwardly at Haron, and then pointed out, 'But look, Imam, I'm safe here in exile. You will be returning home. Are you sure you understand the dangers? They can't get me but they can get you, you know.'

'Don't worry,' stated Haron emphatically. 'You exiles have done your bit, and you continue to fight. I haven't even started yet. I'm still suffering, so I must fight.'

Thus began three hectic weeks. Haron and Abraham drafted and cyclostyled a leaflet for all the South Africans on hadj. They sought out and lobbied members of the Islamic World Council, urging them to intercede with their governments against apartheid. They lobbied fellow South Africans both individually and in groups. With a few exceptions – who turned out mainly to be in the employ of the South African government – they were courteously and attentively received. Some eyebrows were raised at the spectacle of an Imam behaving in this way in Mecca of all places, and some were equally concerned for his safety, warning him that there were government spies among the pilgrims. But most simply admired his courage and drew inspiration from his faith – a faith which affirmed that Islam was not simply about other-worldly concerns but was also about their lives as men and women in the here and now.

By the time they came to leave Mecca, Haron was satisfied that much had been achieved. Change was beginning to seem possible. It was with high hopes therefore that he alighted from

26

the aeroplane at Cairo with a happy wife for company, delighted at the prospect of an extended holiday.

The representatives of the Pan-Africanist Congress that met him in Cairo were strangers. But their warm embraces and enthusiastic welcome made him feel an old comrade straight away. He was entertained at their offices which were provided and subsidized by the Government of Egypt, and he was introduced to officials with whom the PAC had dealings. They too received him warmly and Haron thrilled with pride at the thought that the problems of his countrymen had made a real impact here at the very centre of the Islamic world. Progress, he thought to himself. Yes, progress is being made.

Encouraged by his reception, he felt emboldened to make a request to the Egyptians on a subject dear to his heart – education. Could the Egyptian Government see its way clear to making available educational scholarships for some students to come to Cairo? 'Of course,' came the ready response. 'Resources are available. Arrangements can be made.'

Haron felt greatly inspired by his experiences in Cairo and looked forward to his next port of call, London, with great eagerness therefore. There was no time lost in explaining to him why it was considered so important that he should come. The Pan-Africanist Congress, it was explained, was developing a strategy for armed military struggle. Those who were Haron's old friends and from the same town and community had been assigned to discuss the matter with him and to enlist his help. It would be necessary for him to attend one or two meetings of the PAC where the details could be put to him. What were his feelings?

Haron's old dread of violence had by this time almost completely disappeared but some doubts remained. The bitter lot of the black people of South Africa, coupled with the intransigence and brutality of the State seemed to have legitimized a recourse to armed struggle for its overthrow. His own strength of feeling against the tyranny and oppression had grown in intensity even as the wall of hatred of the black people for the white tyrants grew stronger and higher. He discussed this hatred, sympathized with and justified it but was torn by a contradicition: how can you hate people and claim to be inspired by a non-racial ideal? Moreover, to talk of violence

27

was all very well, but the white State was armed to the teeth whereas the blacks were unarmed and weak. How could the blacks make war when the whites had a monopoly of the means?

But the PAC believed that it had resolved the contradictions. The party was itself non-racial in composition and the abstraction in terms of which 'the system' should be opposed and overthrown while popular hatred was deflected from the living men of flesh and blood who created, sustained and operated that system, had been abandoned. The men of the hateful system were themselves hateful and deserving of hatred. And their hateful system would fall only when they themselves bit the dust or when popular vengance was imminent. Meanwhile the spirit of human brotherhood, the essence of common humanity, the basically unifying and integrationist utilitarian stream which ran through the loftiest thought, ancient and modern, which stood opposed to the divisions, antagonisms and centrifugal forces of racialism and tribalism – these would be expressed through African Nationalism.

Haron's problems and anxieties on questions of armed struggle were soon resolved at meetings with leading members of the PAC. Consequently he became involved in a plan to recruit young men to undertake short courses of guerilla training outside South Africa. They were to leave South Africa ostensibly for a hadj or upon a course of education and then return in the normal way after training. The plan was, then, that Abdulla Haron's role as an Imam would be the perfect cover under which a particularly dangerous form of underground work would be performed. Although this plan was not to meet with any success, its intention was to be viewed by the State with as much gravity as if it had been very successful.

But there was a further matter of great concern to PAC – as, indeed, to the whole political movement – in which the Imam's talents and interests were considered particularly useful. Haron had a long record of work on behalf of the needy and the destitute, and it was desired of him that he in future give special attention to those who were suffering because of their political activities. A deluge of trials and imprisonments, bannings and banishments had produced many destitute men and families. A government which believed in penury, homelessness and starvation as a weapon against its opponents and their families as a means of breaking their will to resist its tyranny, did not believe in providing charity. No 'welfare state', not even a 'work-house' and only very patchy and selective rudiments of even a 'poor law' existed. Even a charity known as the Defence and Aid Fund which had been established by the 'Christian Action' organization founded by Canon John Collins of St Pauls Cathedral, London, in order to help the victims of Apartheid, had been outlawed.

It was urgently pleaded that Haron must extend his charitable work and do whatever was possible to fill the breach and aid the sufferers financially.

The Imam's response was prompt and warm. 'I will certainly do all I can. It is work I love and I am obligated by Islam to undertake it. But, look, we are a poor community and there is therefore, in fact, very little we *can* do!'

'Yes, and we here in exile are poverty-stricken, too,' Haron's comrades replied, 'but we have considered this and believe we have a remedy. As you are known for your welfare work, we are sure that we can prevail upon Canon John Collins to help you financially for this purpose.'

When it had been agreed that Haron would use monies received for charitable purposes only for those purposes and provide proof of this, a meeting with Canon John Collins was arranged.

The Muslim and Christian clerics immediately struck relations of great cordiality and respect despite their contrasting styles. The short, balding Imam showed off his most resplendant Arabian robes uninhibitedly; the erect, greying Canon of Christianity remained sober and restrained in his dark Christian habit. But they shared certain common purposes and it was soon agreed that money would be made available so that Haron could continue and extend his welfare work.

To the effusive thanks of the little Imam on behalf of the oppressed people of South Africa, the Canon quietly and simply responded: 'There are many things that I detest, Imam, but none more than racial oppression. For some years now I have believed that if Christianity is to be seen to work in the world today, then prayer must be coupled with Christian action. The person and work of Jesus Christ must not be allowed to become obscured behind a cloud of theological dogma.'

Eagerly the Imam agreed: men of religion must show every concern for the well-being of people and make their work socially relevant.

'Well, then, Imam,' warned the Canon gently, 'do take care. We cannot afford to lose you.'

The Canon, of course, had uppermost in mind the danger of loss to the community of socially-conscious men of God. As to Haron's recruitment work for PAC, as he was unaware of this he could hardly have suspected how deeply touched was the Imam by the quietly expressed concern. In the event, Haron, always the perky, confident and optimistic one, smiled broadly.

'Don't worry, Canon.' replied Haron in the carefree tones of one totally convinced that Allah protects the righteous whether they come bearing Islamic obligations or Christian charity or, slyly, revolutionary guns. 'I intend being around a long time yet, Allah permitting.'

Haron's commitment to the struggle for liberation could go no further. And, as though to emphasise the point, he, unknown to his wife, carried on their return journey home, a cassette tape-recording of an address from the exiled leadership of PAC to the underground movement in the Cape.

Chapter Four

Underground

Haron returned to South Africa feeling ex-
hilarated. He was well aware that his activities in Mecca would
have been monitored by the Secret Police, but his visits to Cairo
and to London were a different matter. Efforts had been made
to keep these secret. Either way, he remained undaunted. He
knew that three men had recently died in detention, and the
New Year was less than a month old when another death was
announced. No one could be found to believe the State's claim
that all had committed suicide.

As soon as possible Haron arranged to meet Gamat, and so a
clandestine meeting of the PAC group was set up in an area of
the Cape Flats known as the Rylands Estate. The group were
overwhelmed by Haron's enthusiasm and confidence. He had
much to report and his optimism came as an inspiration and an
encouragement at a very difficult period. All agreed that he had
been right to undertake the welfare and recruitment work. But,
remarkably, no one noticed how Haron had been overburdened.
No one noticed the grave mistake in departing from the first
principle of underground work – that of the separation of
functions. Each function would carry risks. The risks were
doubled and the stresses and strains vastly increased. Fortunately
it was agreed that because of his heavy commitments, contact
with Haron would be infrequent.

So the Imam embarked on his new work. This did not mean
that he neglected the activities of his mosque or of the Muslim

31

community. The study groups and the madressas remained important to him, and his Friday sermons continued to attract the faithful from far and wide.

To the forgotten families of political prisoners Haron's visits came like manna from heaven. He helped raise their spirits and enabled them to retain a shred of dignity beneath the crushing burden of the loss of loved ones and bread-winners. Neighbours often remained aloof, 'not wanting trouble', knowing that walls had ears and that the State would not scruple to persecute, not just its enemies and their children, but also any who might befriend them.

Haron found himself under constant surveillance. The informers that had been planted inside his congregation made themselves obvious. This was part of a new technique adopted by the State when it felt itself well on top. The political police began to pay intermittent visits to his home. 'Nothing much – just checking' was the repeatedly declared purpose. Then they would raid the mosque, go through the library and search through everything with a fine tooth-comb. No 'incriminating' documents were found. Haron found it increasingly difficult to continue the relief work because the police were now openly and demonstratively watching his movements. He discovered that his bank accounts were being checked. Informers were growing in number and becoming ever more brazen. In October 1967 the police sprang a trap.

Haron was approached by a neighbour who was claiming to have trouble with the Race Classification Board. They had refused to accept his claim that he was a 'Cape Malay'; would the Imam certify that he was indeed a 'Cape Malay' for legal purposes? Haron had never paid much attention to the various race classification laws and so he obliged his neighbour by certifying that he was indeed what he claimed to be. Immediately he found himself under arrest. Under the terms of this obnoxious law it appeared that the man was in fact an 'Indian'. Haron was fined £50 with legal costs amounting to £400. The police were much entertained by Haron's discomfiture and gave themselves a pat on the back. For his part, Haron rapidly came to the conclusion that in future he must be rigorously law-abiding on matters of detail such as this in order not to jeopardize the vital work on which he was primarily engaged.

Police visits to the Haron home became more frequent. His wife began to show signs of strain. Usually a certain Major Genis would ask one or two questions while a Sergeant Spyker van Wyk glowered menacingly in the background.

Galiema began to plead anxiously: 'Abdulla, please leave politics alone. I can't stand any more.'

Haron had a stock set of responses. 'Galiema, leave it in Allah's hands', 'Have faith', 'Allah knows best'.

Gradually the strain began to tell on Haron. He felt that something had gone wrong. This was reflected in the letters that he sent abroad. Fortunately communication with the rest of the world was relatively simple. His employment as a salesman enabled him to move about the country without arousing suspicion and he had a wide circle of varied contacts who often travelled abroad and could take messages. But his political work was being gravely obstructed. Sometimes he felt it was impossible to continue. The exiles inquired if it might not be best to call a halt and choose exile as they had done. Haron undertook to try and get abroad for consultations as soon as possible.

Members of his congregation also noticed that he seemed under some sort of strain and suggested another holiday abroad. Haron demurred. Information had reached him that the régime was sending agents to such places as Mecca, the Middle East and even London. He decided that it was crucial to discover the identity of as many of these agents as possible. He could not contemplate a holiday as long as there was the prospect of a breakthrough in this area. To his bitter disappointment, it turned out that some were Muslims.

All his efforts proved fruitless, however. He was forced to give the exiles the names of others who could continue his work, in the event of his being forced to flee or if anything worse happened to him. The alternative possibilities, however, were few and were dwindling in number. The political climate remained tense. The State had taken powers to detain people in solitary confinement for three years, after finding first 90 days and then 180 days inadequate. Torture of detainees in these lonely confines was now a matter of routine. There were not many who felt equal to braving this terrible prospect.

Daily, it became easier to walk straight into the arms of the ever watchful police. This nearly happened to Haron one day as he was on his way to see Gamat. He was carrying documents which would have incriminated both of them. Fortunately he had committed to memory a list of the registration numbers of police cars and he spotted one on the list as he neared his destination. Haron ducked into a nearby doorway and waited to see what would happen. Sure enough, who should emerge from the car but Major Genis and Spyker van Wyk. They strolled around, watching and waiting – so Haron left, knowing that something had gone wrong. It subsequently emerged that the meeting was a trap set by a hitherto trusted colleague. So another ally was lost and fresh arrangements had to be made for the meeting with Gamat. But the latter's bad health, together with the strain of continuous police surveillance, was proving too much for him. He decided to leave South Africa and, early in 1968, he departed into exile with his young family. Haron felt that much more alone.

All his spiritual resources were now needed to face up to the pressures upon him. The traditions and tales of the martyrs of Islam became a treasure-house from which he replenished his stock of energy and courage. Just as important was the recent memory of South African patriots who had suffered for the same cause. He was encouraged by the example of those who had spent up to six months in solitary confinement in terrible conditions, and by the heroism of those who had died under torture. By comparison, he felt his sacrifices were as nothing.

In spite of the precariousness of Haron's position, he still felt it to be his duty to comment on the events of the day, however obliquely. The method he chose for this was to recall some of the great epics of Islamic history. Thus on Eid day, the foremost Islamic festival which immediately followed the thirty-day fast of Ramadan, he told the story of the first official of Islam, Bilal, a story which he also published in pamphlet form, as follows:

'Bilal was the son of an Abyssinian slave girl and was sold while a child to Umaiyah bin Khalf, who was a rich man in the Quraish tribe in Mecca.

'As a young man, Bilal listened to the preaching of the Holy Prophet and so became a Muslim. Strong in his conviction, he did not hide his conversion to the unitarian faith of Islam. His

34

master was angry and told him to renounce the faith but Bilal refused. The master gave him cruel blows, but when young Bilal proved adamant he began to inflict torture after torture upon him. He made Bilal lie prostrate on the scorching sands and gravel without food or water but Bilal, instead of giving up the faith, used to cry "Allah Ahad! Allah Ahad!" (God is one! God is one!)

'One day the cruel master tied Bilal hand and foot and, putting a rope round him, ordered street urchins to drag Bilal along the streets of Mecca. Abu Bakar, the companion of the Prophet, saw this and offered to purchase Bilal. He gave the price demanded – a cloak and ten pieces of silver; then, having purchased Bilal, he set him free. Bilal was thus one of the earliest Muslims and a staunch believer, whose faith had stood the acid test of the worst persecution.

'When the Muslims, after emigration to Medina, were organized by the Prophet into a community and the first Mosque was built, it was decided not to ring bells but to recite the Azan (a vocal call) at the times of prayer for calling the faithful. As Bilal was gifted with a powerful and sonorous voice, the choice for the post of first Muezzin (official caller) fell upon him. He was thus the first mosque official in Islamic history.

'By this appointment, the Holy Prophet had not only appointed the right man for the post, but had . . . trampled under his feet discrimination of colour and race!

'He also arranged Bilal's marriage with a lady from a noble Quraish family. Bilal was not only the Muezzin of the Prophet's mosque but was his constant attendant. He accompanied the Prophet in wars. Destiny brought before him, face to face, his cruel ex-master Umaiyah bin Khalf, who fell a victim to Bilal's sword.

'Bilal's love for the Prophet was unparalleled and the Prophet too had a soft spot in his heart for Bilal. The early Muslims loved and respected him as a close companion of the Prophet. He was with the Prophet through thick and thin. He was by the Prophet's side not only in the battlefields but also during the Prophet's triumphant entry to Mecca. And when the Prophet made his historic Farewell Pilgrimage, it was Bilal who walked by the Prophet, shading him with a primitive screen from the noonday sun.

35

'His grief at the demise of the Holy Prophet was so profound that he sought permission to relinquish his post as Muezzin. He had been the Muezzin from the very first day Azan had been chanted; to him, Azan meant the beloved presence of the Prophet. He did not feel like chanting the Azan without the Prophet coming to lead the prayers. He asked Caliph Abu Bakar to permit him to take part in Jehad (holy war) instead, which request was readily granted. He accompanied Abu Ubaida in the Syrian campaign; when Caliph Umar visited Damascus after its conquest, Umar and the other companions of the Prophet pleaded with Bilal to chant Azan once again. And Bilal chanted the Azan, the first and the last time after the Prophet's demise. To put it in the words of an English writer: "When after moments of tremulous watching, the grand voice of the aged African rolled out amid the hush, with the old beloved words, the old familiar tones, still deeper and clearer, Umar and all those about him wept aloud and tears streamed down every warrior's face, and the last notes of the chant were lost in a tempest of sobbing."

'Bilal is described as a tall, lean man with a stooping gait; his complexion was dark, his face thin and his thick hair strongly tinged with grey. He died in 28 A.H. (After Hejira) at the age of sixty in Dariya, Saudi Arabia.'

The story's message was clear to one and all. These are bad times for the black people. Oppression is in the air. Torture is rife. But keep the faith. A time will come when the oppressors who turn like mad beasts on their fellow men will obtain their just deserts. The colour of a man's skin is no measure of his manhood.

For reasons of their own the authorities took no action to confiscate Haron's passport. This gave him a false sense of security. He believed that they had their suspicions but were nowhere near the truth. The passport was due to expire in March 1969 so if he was to consult his comrades in exile it would have to be before then. His preparations to depart for Mecca in December 1968 were not disturbed in any way by the police. December therefore found him once more in Mecca, this time not accompanied by his wife. He did not, however, dally long but proceeded with as much haste as Islamic decorum would allow to Cairo.

Haron was well received by high officials of the Egyptian administration and was able quickly to transact his business in Cairo. On his way to London he stopped over at Leyden in Holland to consult with Lars Gunnar Ericksson, Director of the International University Exchange Fund. Haron was still deeply interested in arranging facilities for the education of the black youth of South Africa, and on this occasion he was also anxious to make arrangements for his own elder daughter, who had already done the hadj and was now waiting to continue her studies in England. The burly Swede found Haron apparently calm and confident.

It was only when he reached London and met again those people to whom he felt closest that Haron was at last able to unburden himself. He told them that there were informers everywhere, that he was being continuously harassed by the Special Branch, that they were trying to persuade his employers to fire him.

'But my employers understand my position and are prepared to transfer me to an overseas branch if necessary. The fact is, though, that as things stand I can only be a danger to others. I'm beginning to find out for myself what all of you went through. Every knock on the door has become a nightmare for Galiema and the whole family.'

'My God,' said Mujaheed, 'you're in grave danger. We must get you out of there.'

The problem was: how much did the political police know and how did they get their information? This was discussed at length; then they reviewed the records of all those who had taken part in any of the planning sessions or who had been informed of their outcome. It remained a mystery. Perhaps after all the police did not know that much. Those who were aware of Haron's activities all appeared to be entirely trustworthy. It was nevertheless suggested to Haron that he should simply remain abroad, give up the idea of returning to South Africa altogether, and choose exile. He was agonized by the prospect of being torn from his country, family, friends, mosque and congregation and all that he had fought so hard for. The issue had been broached previously in conversation, but otherwise he had not discussed it with a soul. It was a great relief to do so now. In the end, however, it was a matter that only Haron could decide. He had unfinished business to complete and his suggestion was that if his passport was not renewed when it expired in March 1969 he would know that the time had come to leave.

Before he left London he had a last meeting with Canon Collins who also urged him to consider exile. But Haron re-affirmed his faith in the protection of Allah and promised to be as careful as possible. There was nothing more to be said.

Mujaheed accompanied him to the Air Terminal for a last few words of farewell and encouragement. Here Haron once more voiced a concern that was close to his heart. 'Please,' he begged, 'take care of my daughter. Treat her as your own. See that she completes her education. Teach her to serve her people well.'

Mujaheed reassured him, urging him at the same time to take all possible care of himself. Haron smiled, embraced his friend, turned and made his way down the escalator.

Back in South Africa he sets about the work he has under-taken to do. This includes extending the field of operations among 'political families' in country districts. On 4 March he advises that things are going as planned, but by 22 March a grave shortage of money is hampering his efforts.

'Things are very grim for the fighters up country,' he reports. 'It is up to you to cheer them up.'

Meanwhile he applies to the authorities for permission to go over to Robben Island to visit Kathy Kathrada, one of the Rivonia trialists imprisoned far from his Johannesburg home. This information is the cause of considerable alarm in London because such a request, routine in any other country, in South Africa can only attract the attention of the Security Police. Haron reassures them. His motives will be seen as purely humanitarian and he is proceeding with extreme caution. He takes to getting up very early in the morning for work, thus avoiding the army of informers who are still catching up on the sleep they have lost watching him and others the night before. His job, which in any case takes him all round the country, is a help and he continues to seek out reliable contacts wherever he can. He develops an instinct for spotting collaborators which often involves him in beating a hasty if strategic retreat. He operates with stealth and cunning but, notwithstanding all this, the superior machinery of the political police cannot be avoided altogether. As Haron throws himself into his work with a last furious bout of energy so the net slowly closes around him.

His passport expires and when he applies for its renewal there is only silence from the authorities. Things look ominous. Haron busies himself with school fêtes and functions, with the work of the madressas, with prize-givings and so on. He advises London that his daughter should not be allowed home under any circumstances.

Then in May 1969 the police make their move. He is required to report to their headquarters in the city and is questioned. To his astonishment they show him a thick file containing information about his two journeys overseas and they give him the names of Mujaheed and Abraham as contacts he has made abroad. Calmly he denies all their claims. They only smile and say menacingly, 'We are not finished with you yet!'

The most dangerous moment has arrived. What to do?

He considers going through the formality of applying for an exit visa, while at the same time making alternative arrangements for the receipt of money from abroad. But it is hard for him to decide any more whether his actions are the result of careful planning or of panic and fear. He is followed all the time, particularly when he goes on his rounds to the black African townships. When he leaves his mosque in the evening to go home in his car he is tailed – their front bumper nudging his rear one. They are making sure that they have him under surveillance twenty-four hours a day – and that he knows it.

Is flight possible? It appears the only way out. But Haron is being worn down to a state of inactivity bordering on paralysis in which all seems hopeless and escape inconceivable. The tension is now unbearable. Only sleep brings a few hours of relief. Outwardly though he appears calm, and on 23 May he is to be found making a presentation of prizes to the children at a madressa in a neighbouring township.

Haron resolves his dilemma whether or not he should go into exile, but in order to do so he needs to outwit his guards. He is worried too at the prospect that his effort to escape might endanger others who would have to hide him. He is in fact too tired to think straight and that is most dangerous of all. In the end he can only fall back on his unbounded confidence in Allah to protect His loyal servant. For Haron, even now, 'Allah knows best'. In a sense his every action or even lack of action is determined by the one true God; whatever happens finally will be the will of Allah. Allah will stand by him at the hour of his greatest trial should the need arise.

Chapter Five

Arrest

Early on the morning of 'Milad un' Nabie' which in 1969 fell on 28 May, Spyker van Wyk and one of his cohorts at the Security Branch, Western Cape, went to the home of Abdulla Haron to make their arrest. Haron was at home that day and was happy and high-spirited because the birthday of the prophet Muhammad was an important day for him. Thousands of Muslims would be gathering at their various mosques in the evening, and it was important that their Imams lead the celebrations in a joyful frame of mind. The visit of Spyker and his colleague therefore came as a most unwelcome, even profane, intrusion.

Spyker was also very happy that day. Taking Abdulla Haron into detention on the day which was both the Prophet's birthday and the anniversary of his appointment as Imam was an event to be savoured. Although he could hardly contain his perverted glee, Spyker's feeling of power enabled him to put on a show of courtesy and consideration.

'Imam Haron, the Major would like to see you at Caledon Square. Just a few questions, you know. So we would like you to accompany us, please,' came the polite request to the disappointed Imam. But Abdulla Haron knew that it was not within the power of a South African citizen – particularly a coloured one – to deny these 'polite' requests.

'Oh . . . Look, you know it's the Prophet's birthday today . . .

41

I have a lot to do . . . Will the Major be long?' Haron was in fact anxious for more reasons than just the Prophet's birthday. They had not really come to ask him politely to come to Caledon Square. They had come to collect him. Could this be the long-dreaded detention? Whatever the true position, he must not show alarm in front of his wife.

'Just a little talk, Imam,' said Spyker civilly. He was thoroughly enjoying the cat-and-mouse game. He continued with the barest hint of menace in his voice, 'How long it takes depends on you, of course.'

'Well, all right then,' replied Haron resignedly, 'I'll see you later, Galiema. Don't worry. Just see that my robes are ready for tonight's service.'

Galiema Haron was worried as she watched the police-car disappear down the road. There had been something sinister about Spyker's very courtesy. He had the ugliest imaginable close-set eyes blazing out of a lean face, and at the best of times an aura of malice seemed to surround him. Even Galiema, who did not have the slightest connection with politics, had come to know about him.

Spyker van Wyk had long been well known in the streets of District Six among small shopkeepers, criminals and mis-creants, from the days when he had been a detective in the Criminal Investigation Department. This renown derived from his abuse of police powers in terrorizing anyone he came up against. His blackmailing of small shopkeepers for free cigarettes and his demands for small bribes for closing his eyes to after-hours' trading had gained for him a widespread hatred. The increased powers he acquired after transferring to the Security Branch (S.B.) gave Spyker the opportunity to try to settle many old scores, but he also suffered many frustrations. In the days before the reign of terror began in 1963, the law courts had acted to uphold some measure of legality, and many cases were lost by the police. Spyker was involved in so many lost cases that he tended to view the courts, and even the law itself, as a gross interference in his activities.

There was hardly a public meeting held where Spyker could not be observed hovering in the background, scarcely a raid on or a search of a private house with which he was not connected. He went about his work with an enthusiasm which was characterized by his relentless harassment of anyone he over-heard expressing a liberal idea. And when the reign of terror removed the inconvenient, if distant, surveillance of the judi-ciary for all practical purposes, Spyker became involved in physical assaults upon prisoners and detainees. Alan Brookes and Stephanie Kemp, political detainees currently resident in Britain, were both seriously assaulted by Spyker van Wyk.

Galiema Haron had every reason to feel worried. Spyker van Wyk had been altogether too frequent a visitor to her home recently, and had on one visit brazenly declared that he had actually been watching her husband very closely since 1960!

As the car sped along Haron's mind was in a ferment of activity. Could this be it? He was glad Shamela was overseas! But perhaps it would have been better for her to have been at home with her mother? Must get the story clear in his mind. Must remember: the first days were the most dangerous. Why hadn't he fled? Would it have been better to have remained in London in December? Would they detain him? They couldn't prove anything! Or could they? Spyker was being far too polite. They're on to something! No! No need to worry! Would his being an Imam be any protection against ill-treatment? What would his congregation say? Do? Oh, God! Those files they had shown him!

Soon Haron found himself in the inner sanctum of the head-quarters of the political police, a dark brick building sur-rounded on all four sides by busy streets. Known as Caledon Square, it accommodates Cape Town's central police station, including the Vice Squad, Fraud Squad, Immorality Squad and the ancillary wings. The building also contains detention cells. Haron was escorted into a waiting-room and left on his own. As the hours went by his inner tension grew. Occasionally a police officer would come into the room, look straight at him and shake his head. Before Haron could inquire as to the whereabouts of Spyker, the officer would withdraw. Finally Major Genis and Spyker entered the room together.

'Ugh, man Imam! So sorry to keep you waiting. But we are very busy, looking into some other matters,' said the stocky Major with an apologetic even if disingenuous smile. 'Now, look, we have an important appointment at this moment and we

43

will get down to our talks after two o'clock. Alright? Then, see you later.'

No answer was called for from Haron. He was being told, not asked. He simply looked nonplussed as the Major and Spyker withdrew.

He did not know Genis very well although he had seen something of him of late. Genis had become attached to the Cape Security Branch in 1965, but he generally seemed to leave the foot-slogging and the dirty work to his minions, choosing for himself a polite and sensitive background role. But what Genis's role was to be now, Haron realized, he could only wait and see.

Spyker adjourned to his paperback novel and Genis to his sandwich lunch and his newspaper. The newspaper was full of reports of Vorster's cancellation of the England cricket team's tour of South Africa because of the inclusion of the Cape Coloured, Basil D'Oliveira, in the English team. This dictation to the MCC by the Anti-Apartheid Movement infuriated the Major, but he was pleased that D'Oliveira was 'not allowing himself to be used as propaganda against South Africa'. If only all 'non-whites' were so level-headed, he thought wishfully.

At 2.00 p.m. Haron was conducted to the interrogation room. There he found Genis with a large file before him and Spyker tapping a ball-point impatiently on a notebook. Haron was feeling highly keyed-up as he sat down at the far end of the large table.

Genis cleared his throat. Formality now cut across the politeness he had shown earlier in the day. 'We are not satisfied with the explanations you gave about your two trips overseas. I refer to December, 1966, and to your last visit in 1968. We have reason to believe that you were engaged in activities over there about which you have not told us. In fact, that you are concealing vital matters. Now then, are you prepared to enlarge on those visits?'

'I have told you already about those visits,' Haron replied, sounding as aggrieved as possible. 'There is nothing more I can tell you. I went on pilgrimage and also took a holiday. I visited London to arrange for my daughter's education. That's all!'

Spyker put down his ball-point and, looking menacingly at Haron, burst out, 'You know you are lying, man! You're a

44

priest! Don't you feel ashamed of lying?'

Genis intervened. 'Look, Imam, here is a chance I'm giving you – make a full statement and you will be able to walk out of here now with no more trouble from us.'

Suddenly Haron realized that his suspicions had been confirmed. This was no ordinary interview. He might be detained. If it was to be, Allah knew best.

Spyker laughed maliciously. 'We're not such fools as you think, man! Your game's up! There's no point in telling stories now, man!' He was cocky.

'I've told you everything,' repeated Haron with an air of puzzlement.

'You shouldn't be so stubborn, you know,' said Genis calmly, ignoring the feigned puzzlement. 'We know everything about you and all your activities. Here and overseas . . . It's all here in this file. So there is no point in withholding information.'

Haron smiled. 'What I don't understand is this: if you know everything, why do you want me to give you information?'

Genis and Spyker made a great show of not allowing themselves to be irritated.

'Well,' said Genis after a moment, 'we've got a procedure you see . . . All we want is to fill in a few details. We've got nothing against you personally, Imam. We know you are not a Communist. But we can't allow you to be used by the Communists. So if you talk, everything can be settled quickly.' The smile vanished and his eyes hardened as he looked directly at Haron.

'Man, you are in the shit, man! So you better talk!' shouted Spyker, banging on the table.

Haron observed the policemen carefully. God, how many times have you devils tried this trick to get people to put a noose around their own necks? he thought. Now I'm supposed to tell the truth to liars like you!

'No, Major, I can't help you any more,' he said quietly, happy that his voice betrayed no fear.

Genis looked stern. Solemnly he said, 'Abdulla Haron, I am placing you under arrest and by virtue of section 6(1) of the Terrorism Act of 1967, you will be detained indefinitely. You will not be permitted any visitors except a magistrate fortnightly. And you will be kept in solitary confinement.'

Spyker smiled broadly. Triumphantly he banged the table. 'Now perhaps you will answer the questions!'

Haron blanched. He had been expecting it but the final confirmation nevertheless came as an unpleasant shock. However, he must remain true to himself. Sacrifices must be made in the cause. He must place his faith in Allah. Allah will come to the aid of his loyal servant. Silently, he looked at Genis and then at Spyker.

'Now then,' Genis started off again, 'let me ask you once more. I want a true and complete statement of your activities while you were overseas: the people you made contact with, what you discussed, and the rest of it.'

Once more they covered the ground they had already gone over. Once more Haron could add nothing to what he had previously said. Finally the Major turned to Spyker. 'You will now proceed to the detainee's house and make a search.' To the Imam he said, 'At your house you will be permitted to take your Bible, your toothbrush, and so on. You may only speak to your family in the presence of the police officers, and to nobody else.'

It was evening when the police arrived at Haron's home. Galiema was now extremely anxious. She had had no word of her husband's whereabouts all day. Haron had been wondering how to soften the effect that the news of his detention would have on her and the children, but he was given no chance. Galiema came running to the door.

'Imam, what's happened?' she asked anxiously.

Spyker cut Haron short before he could speak.

'Your man has been placed under arrest and he will be detained indefinitely!' And then, shouting out each word like a hammer blow, 'And-you-will-not-be-allowed-to-see-him-while-he-is-in-solitary-confinement!' Ignoring Galiema's cry of horror, he snapped at Haron, 'You will not talk to your wife unnecessarily, otherwise we will lock her up too! Now come, so that we can get this search done.'

Spyker felt pleased. He got enormous pleasure out of his work. He liked hurting the families of the opponents of the régime, even down to the children. Before the spate of Draconian legislation had given legality to every Gestapo-like excess, Spyker had felt like an Olympic sprinter in a sack race. He had been suspected of organizing a gang of masked thugs to break into the homes of political activists to terrorize the wives when their husbands were out, and to throw petrol bombs – at night – at the same homes. Now he found himself presented with limitless opportunities to practise a different kind of terror, with the full force of the law behind him. His was no mere job: it was a vocation and a pleasure.

Abdulla Haron looked at his wife; she seemed on the verge of tears. He shrugged his shoulders helplessly and said, 'Don't worry, Galiema. Leave it in Allah's hands. Everything will be all right, Inshallah. Take the children out of the way, meanwhile. I'll talk to you when they are finished with their search.'

Spyker methodically searched Haron's desk and placed bank statements in his brief-case. He fingered Haron's books, occasionally picking one out, holding it up and shaking it for notes. He empied the drawers and cupboards, searched through the pockets of the clothing, looked under carpets, tapped on the walls and peered behind pictures. He was thorough and took his time. He did not show his disappointment at finding nothing of an incriminating nature.

The search was finished. The policemen were now in a hurry to leave. Spyker addressed Haron. 'You can bring your Bible and things. And pyjamas if you like.' He informed Galiema, 'You can bring your man a change of clothing once a week and hand it in at the charge office at Caledon Square. That's all.'

'His food! What about his food?' gasped the anxious Galiema.

'He can eat the food we give him! What's the matter with our food?' bellowed Spyker.

'It's not halal and my husband eats only halal food!' replied Galiema briskly, with the confidence women acquire when men intrude into their realm.

'Well,' responded Spyker less confidently, 'I will talk to Major Genis about that. Come, it's late. We must go.'

Haron embraced his wife, 'Don't worry, I'll be all right. Just pray,' he said reassuringly. He hugged the 13-year-old Mohammed and, holding him at arm's length, said, 'You are the man of the house while I am away. Look after your mother and sister.' He picked up the bewildered 6-year-old Fatima and kissed her.

Galiema had got together the various things Spyker had mentioned, but had included also a prayer-rug. These the Imam picked up. He was ready to go. As Spyker and his colleague escorted her husband out of the house, Galiema burst out crying and hugged her little daughter close to her in a desperate protective gesture. The young Mohammed rushed upstairs to the balcony. 'Daddy! Daddy!' he wailed. But his despairing cries were lost in the revving of the noisy Volkswagen outside. For him childhood ended at that moment; the awful train of events had swept him into manhood at the tender age of 13. This would be the family's last sight of a husband, a father and a religious leader who was still alive.

To the congregation of the Al Jaamia mosque, the news of the Imam's arrest and detention came as a shock, coupled initially with disbelief. Then gradually the celebrations to mark the birth of the prophet Muhammad turned into a wake. Many wept openly. A number of young men had been expecting trouble for the Imam, but even they were nevertheless taken aback by the suddenness of the event. As the congregation began to pray for their Imam, these young men rushed out to carry the bad tidings to other mosques. The question on everyone's lips was 'Why on the Prophet's birthday?' Was this another example of white Christian arrogance cocking a snook at Islam?

Haron was returned to Caledon Square at 10.00 p.m. that evening. In a little room adjoining the cells he was searched and then 'booked in'. He was led up some stairs through heavy barred gates and along a corridor to cell 164. Along the left-hand side was a row of doors made of solid steel. In each door, at eye-level, was a peep-hole covered on the outside by a small steel flap. On the inside of the peep-hole was a sheet of glass which was placed there to prevent the inmates of the cell from moving the steel flap aside to look out. From the outside, the viewer had a panoramic view of each cell and its prisoners. In some cells brave or foolhardy prisoners had smashed the glass plate and even the steel flap.

Haron gazed in horror at the steel door with its tiny peep-hole. He entered the cell and was all but overcome by claustrophobia as he observed its dimensions. The cell was about five feet wide and about seven feet long. Seven feet up the far wall was a window overlooking the side-street. The window, which was protected by thick steel bars, was further protected from both inside and outside by heavy wire-mesh in frames which were bolted to the walls. Years of dust covered everything between the inner and outer frames of mesh and admitted almost no light from the outside. The sun, which in any case never shone from the south, would never penetrate into the cell. In the ceiling was an electric light covered with very thick glass which was also rendered inaccessible by wire-mesh bolted on to the ceiling. The light burned all night and often all day as well, but was too weak to read by, and yet bright enough to interfere with sleep. The lower half of the walls was painted in 'regulation' brown to hide the filth, and the distempered white of the upper half and the ceiling had turned grey with age. The sole distraction from the oppressive lack of space and the monotonous loneliness was the noise from the street below the window – a reminder that, outside, life went on as normal. Sensory deprivation was further lessened by the drawings, messages and slogans pencilled and scratched on the walls by previous prisoners, so desperate to express their humanity and communicate their thoughts that they had risked the terrifying wrath of the great South African police to do so.

Haron observed the smirks on the faces of his captors as they witnessed the horror which flitted momentarily across his face. He forced himself to put on a brave show in their presence, but his heart was racing. God, he thought, is this how they treat our people? As his jailers withdrew to a slamming of doors and gates and a horrible rattling of keys, he slowly began to regain his composure.

Alone at last after a long day, he methodically arranged the blankets which were to be his bed and laid out his prayer-mat. He had been warned that he had to take care about arranging his blankets: they had to be smoothed out without bumps or folds in them because, lying on the hard concrete floor, every bump or fold would press against his body like a mighty beam and produce great discomfort. He made a space for his Koran and the other things, and sat down on his bed. So this is it, he said to himself. Now begins the long silence, the long loneliness, the grilling. He must remember what friends had told him about their experiences. He must establish a regimen to which he must adhere in a strictly disciplined way.

49

He must not forget his prayers. Allah is great; Allah is merciful; Allah would protect his loyal servant in his hour of need; Allah knows best; he must keep faith and place his trust in Allah. He had missed some of his obligatory prayers earlier that day and must make up for it now. Perhaps there was a special message in his being detained on the birthday of the Prophet Muhammad. His midnight prayers must for all these reasons be very special. He must pray now as he had never prayed in his life before. He knew Galiema and the children would be praying for him, and all his friends would be praying, too. His loyal congregation would have missed his leadership at the mosque this evening but they would understand. And they would say special prayers for him.

What should be the routine he should follow during his imprisonment? A few moments were needed to think about this. If, as a result of the demands of his captors, he missed his prayers, he must make up for it later. There were five obligatory prayers and the non-obligatory midnight prayer, which he had always, in any case, said. He would fast during the day and have one meal each night. The food must be halal and must therefore come from home. Galiema would see to that. Fasting would be no problem. Twenty years ago when he was studying in Mecca he had been asked by his tutor what he intended to do for Islam. He was not a wealthy man and had therefore said that for the rest of his life he would fast on Mondays and Thursdays as thanksgiving to his creator. He had kept his pledge ever since. Fasting would be no difficulty.

And the fasting would help his motions. No need to use a latrine-pail then. Nor any need to keep having to beg the warders to let him go to the communal lavatory down the corridor. He would be able to use the lavatory in the mornings. When he had the opportunity, he would walk vigorously about the yard. That would help him to suffer the confinement better and would sustain his morale. He would also do some physical jerks in his cell. He must keep physically fit, and not allow himself to deteriorate either physically or mentally. That would keep him alert to the tricks of his captors.

He would also stick to the story he had given the police. Everything he had done was for Islam and in furtherance of his religious obligations. If the worst came to the worst, he would

50

take all the guilt upon himself. He would not divulge who was with him. Now he must pray and then he must sleep.

The news of the Imam's detention had meanwhile spread like wildfire. Hardly had Haron been closeted in his cell, than a group of people led by Sheikh Nazeem, a good friend and religious colleague, visited Caledon Square to inquire after his well-being. The tall, dignified Nazeem, attired in his religious robes, approached the police officer in the charge-office. There, a burly, white uniformed policeman who did not appreciate this show of concern gave them short shrift: it was none of their business and 'if you're troublesome we'll lock up the lot of you, too!' The group retreated.

Thus even the innocent inquiries of well-intentioned friends, including a highly respected priest, met with a humiliating rebuff. How many thousands of concerned friends would have been needed, for any other kind of response to have been forthcoming? Who can tell?

Chapter Six

Interrogation: The First Day

*The problems of writing about the interrogation
of Haron must be apparent to the reader. It is in the nature of
the subject that only the torturers and their victims are present.
No confession from the interrogators has been forthcoming and
is hardly likely to be made; their victim in this case is dead. The
authors have here constructed an interrogation, without which the
story of Abdulla Haron would be incomplete, on the basis of their
knowledge of his political work, from a letter smuggled out of his
prison by Haron, and from the collective experience of South
African detainees. References are made within the text to facts,
or the police version of them, which emerged at the inquest into
Haron's death, and also to the experiences of others. We believe
that the conversations, interrogations and events as described
may quite reasonably be inferred from all these sources.*

Early on the Thursday morning, the first full day of his
detention, Abdulla Haron was awake and saying his 'Subuh'
(sunrise prayers). A clatter of keys and crash of gates and doors
and muffled shouting announced the arrival of breakfast. Like
all the meals in the police cells, breakfast consisted of two slices
of bread and a mug of coffee. Haron was provided with a mug
but chose water and rejected the two thick slices of brown bread.
His dietary regimen had begun. He was to fast all day and have
one meal, sent from home by his wife, at night.

Haron had noticed the other prisoners in the corridor when they were getting their breakfast. And they looked at him curiously too. Despite his own grim situation, he could not help taking an interest in other people, and this brought to mind the scribblings, drawings and scratchings on the walls of his cell. Here were the stories of others who had passed this way before. He could learn something of these men and briefly take his mind off his own plight. He puckered his brows and strained his eyes and smiled as he read:

All police are pigs.
The Boere are swines – signed The Killers.
Five years for armed robbery no justice – J.T.
Mary my darling I did it for you: I miss you – Koos.
Oh Jesus Christ help me get out of this stincking place – Mickey.
Crime does not pay 9 months for pick-pocketing R2 – signed Blondie.
A bottle of brandy and a lekker girl. That would be heaven now.
The bastard Cockeye turned crown – I'll kill him – The Kid. Help!
Just one smoke Please please
The magistrate was fucking unfair. Drop dead. – signed Tapie.
Kathleen please be true to me. I love you – Piet.

The unfriendly wall of this miserable cell, he ruminated, was a chronicle of the realities of life for the people. In some stolen moment the overpowering human need for self-expression had transferred to these walls deep and raging emotions: contempt and hatred of the police, forlorn calls to God for deliverance, the desperate need for a bottle and a moment of drunken relief. The very passions and contradictions of life itself.

Suddenly Spyker appeared at the door. Further questioning.

The **Inquest** *into Haron's death:*
COOPER : *He was arrested and taken into custody on the 28th May, 1969?*
VAN WYK : *Yes.*
COOPER : *How soon after that did the interrogation commence?*

van Wyk : *Well he was interrogated the same day.*

Cooper : *And on that day he wanted to make a statement? He wanted to give the information you wanted?*

van Wyk : *Yes . . . The statement that he made at that stage was patently false and we were not satisfied, and after two days we told him that we did not believe his story.*

Cooper : *. . . what about the whole of June?*

van Wyk : *He was under constant interrogation daily.*

Cooper : *Throughout the whole of June.*

van Wyk : *Yes.*

Spyker took Haron along to the interrogation room. There Major Genis was waiting there, hefty files placed carefully in front of him.

'Now then, Imam Haron,' purred Genis efficiently, 'you've been getting up to some funny business and we can't allow that. Now you can give us certain information and if you decide to talk it will be much easier for you. So what is it to be?'

Oh, so now it is a matter of 'easier' for me, thought Haron. He struggled not to let his tension show and replied calmly enough: 'I've told you, Major – everything I do is for my religion. I've got nothing to do with anything else. What I do is for Islam and I see no harm in that.'

'Let me make the position clear to you,' said Genis gravely, 'We have good reason to believe the following: (a) you were in touch with a known terrorist when you were in Mecca in 1966; (b) together with this terrorist you were involved in certain activities directed against the policies of the government; (c) you were also in Cairo in 1966 and you associated with certain terrorists there as well; (d) from Cairo you went to London and there also you met certain known terrorists; (e) in 1968 you again met the same terrorists in London and, together with them, conspired against the government. I want to know everything about what you did and what you discussed with these people you met. You will not be released until we have a full statement from you about these matters. Which means that you could be here a really long time if you insist on being stubborn.'

'Imam, man, you can see you are in a serious position, man. You have been caught out and you might as well talk, man,' chimed in Spyker persuasively.

God, thought Haron, I've already answered their questions about all this more than once. They must have something. But I can't give in now.

He shrugged and pointed out to Genis. 'I've given you full explanations about that more than once, Major.'

'I am not satisfied with your explanations,' answered Genis. 'I believe you also received certain instructions from these terrorists. I also want to know what those instructions were.'

'No, no,' answered Haron patiently, 'those were private visits. I received no instructions from anyone. And even if they tried to give me instructions I would not pay any attention.'

'You're lying,' shouted Spyker, 'we have checked your explanations and they don't fit in with our information. You're a crooked priest and now you've been exposed.'

'Look, Imam Haron,' said Genis blandly, 'I know you are a good family man. I too am a family man and I don't like keeping a man away from his family like this. If you cooperate you can be back with your family in next to no time.'

Now it's out of here in next to no time, is it! Hell, how these people change their tune, thought Haron.

'I'm sorry, Major, I've told you everything I know and given you reasonable explanations for everything,' replied Haron carefully.

Genis looked him over. I don't want this man withdrawing into a shell, he thought. Better to let him talk and try to catch him out, try to break down his story. Perhaps he'll tell the truth when he realizes his story is full of flaws.

'All right, Imam', said Genis in a friendly manner, 'if that is your story, let us start at the beginning and go over it again. Start from when you arrived in Mecca and go over everything you did from then on.' Spyker switched on a tape-recorder and then poised his ball-point carefully on his notebook. Haron regarded the two policemen carefully. No point in holding back on what happened in Mecca, he thought, that is public knowledge. Slowly and carefully he proceeded to relate everything that had happened and all he had done in Mecca.

'How did you happen to meet that coolie, Abraham?' demanded Spyker.

'He came to my place,' explained Haron patiently.

'That seems too much of a coincidence,' interjected Genis.

56

'Who arranged for you to meet?'

'No one,' answered Haron, 'it *was* just a coincidence. He must have heard that I was in Mecca and, as we have known each other a long time, he came to see me.'

'Hm. All right, go on,' muttered Genis.

Haron continued.

'Who was this person who printed the leaflets for you?' interjected Genis.

'He is an Arabian friend of mine,' answered Haron. 'He felt he would like to make a donation to our cause.'

'Cause?' blurted out Spyker, his eyebrows jumping as high as they could go.

'Our fight against the Group Areas and such things,' explained Haron.

'All right, go on,' said Genis patiently.

Haron rambled on slowly and expansively.

'Who are the people who helped you give out the leaflets?' interrupted Genis.

'Oh, I don't know any of them, apart from Abraham. I just know they were from South Africa,' parried Haron.

'You're just trying to hide their identities, aren't you,' asserted Spyker forcefully.

'No, I don't know who they were. How can I give you their names if I didn't ask? Anyway, I wouldn't be able to remember today even if I had asked,' Haron brushed the question aside.

'OK. It's almost lunchtime now,' said Genis. 'The sergeant will take you back to your cell. We will continue after lunch.' He felt he was striking the right note of relaxation required to encourage Haron to keep talking. He got up to leave.

'Talking about lunch, Major,' intervened Haron, 'I only eat halal food, and my wife will be bringing my food from home. I hope that will be all right?'

'All right,' said Genis courteously, 'I'll give instructions about it.'

Back in his cell, Haron turned to Spyker and, assuming a querulous tone, remarked, 'Look here, you can't just lock me up again and then come and fetch me for more questioning after you've had your lunch. I haven't had any time in the exercise yard today. I'm entitled to an hour.'

Spyker looked exasperated. 'All right, all right. I'll tell the warder.' He was annoyed and regarded Haron's insistence on his rights as an outrage.

Haron smirked. That's fine, he thought. He was pleased that he had stood up to the interrogation throughout the morning. The first few days are the most dangerous, he repeated to himself. He felt good at having stood up to Spyker's bullying, too, and at having had the courage to demand his hour's exercise. There was little enough opportunity to get into the fresh air and he must seize every chance. He was fasting and so had no use for a lunchtime. It was Thursday, the day he always fasted since making his pledge to his tutor in Mecca as a young man. He used the lavatory and had a delicious and much needed drink of water. Then out into the fresh air of the exercise yard. He knelt and said his midday prayer before walking vigorously about the yard.

The warders had been given strict instructions not to talk to the prisoner in cell 164, and so Haron was left completely alone in the exercise yard, the warder having retired to the far end of the corridor.

Haron looked at the high walls on all four sides and was suddenly struck by a thought: how strange that neither he nor any of his friends, nor anyone else he could remember, had thought about assisting in the escape of a detainee trapped here. True, it was broad daylight when the detainee came out for exercise but, surely, a quick and daring action would succeed? Something like a rope ladder over the wall, for example. Thoughtlessness . . . Inexperience. It takes a long time for a line of thought to take root and become a habit and a way of life. Nothing to do but go on with the struggle; such thoughts will take root eventually and the habits will grow.

Too soon, Haron was back in his cell. He could sit on his blanket-bed for only a few minutes before the unwelcome arrival of Spyker announced the start of another period of interrogation.

Genis was his usual polite and patient self. 'Now yes, Imam. You were unable to give us the names of the people who helped you give out leaflets. You've got a very selective memory. Very convenient.' He hummed quietly to himself. 'Anyway, what about this Islamic World Council or whatever it is called? Who were the members you spoke to?'

'I spoke to all I could get hold of,' answered Haron. 'I don't know their names but it's easy to check the names of the members because it is no secret.'

'You suffer from strange lapses of memory when it comes to names, don't you? What countries were they from? The ones you spoke to, that is,' persisted Genis.

Such detail, thought Haron. My God, they really want you to spill your guts!

'Major, you can think of any country you like, and I spoke to people from that country,' he answered calmly.

'Do you think it is right for a man to go outside his country and make propaganda against his government?' asked Genis.

Spyker leaned forward, very interested in noting the answer to this question.

'I said nothing more than I have said many times from the mimbar,' replied Haron confidently, 'and I don't think the things the government is doing are right. Yet, either we are taken no notice of, or we are treated like criminals when we object. We are quite entitled to ask other people for help if we have no rights ourselves.'

'Ugh! you are talking nonsense!' groaned Spyker loudly. 'If you think we're going to let other countries interfere in our domestic affairs, you've got another think coming. You're an enemy of South Africa, that's what you are!'

Haron gazed back at him silently.

'Then you went to Cairo. I want to hear about that now. Why did you go to Cairo? Where did the money come from? Who did you meet? What did you do there?' demanded Genis.

'I told you, I went on holiday,' said Haron. 'I promised my wife I would give her a holiday. I have friends in Cairo whom I have known for a long time. I had my own money because I saved up . . .' And so on and so on.

'So you only met old acquaintances in Cairo?' interrupted Genis. 'What about the reception you attended? Whom did you meet there?'

'Oh, I forgot about that!' Haron was very surprised about the mention of the reception he had attended, but he calmly pretended a slip of the memory. 'Yes, I was invited to a government reception for the visiting Iraqi Prime Minister.'

'And how is it that you got invited to such a reception?' asked Genis.

HARON : The Minister for National Guidance, Mr Fayek, invited me.

GENIS : Is this Mr Fayek one of your old acquaintances?

HARON : No, I met him during my visit.

GENIS : How did you meet him?

HARON : I arranged an appointment.

GENIS : Could I suggest that your terrorist friends arranged the appointment? After all, these governments are against South Africa and offer their support to all subversive elements.

HARON : No, I arranged my own appointment with the help of my friends.

GENIS : Why did you want to see this Mr Fayek?

HARON : I wanted to ask the government of the United Arab Republic to assist with scholarships for students to study at Al Azhar University.

GENIS : Oh, yes, you have stated this previously. Why do you want scholarships for students to go and study in Cairo? Why can't they study here?

HARON : We get a second-class education here. And there aren't any scholarships, anyway. Even the big multi-national companies keep their scholarships for whites.

Spyker had been restraining himself with some difficulty but now he interjected: 'Ugh! this is Communist propaganda again! Now you are beginning to talk like a Communist yourself. You'd better be careful!'

HARON : I'm not a Communist and never have been. In fact, one of the reasons why I think it is good for students to go to the UAR is because they can learn about Islam and keep away from Communism.

GENIS : You know, of course, that Egypt has good relations with Russia. And the place is overrun with Russian propagandists. How can you say that it is good for students to go to a country like that?

HARON : I've never met one Communist in Egypt. I don't think the students will be in any danger.

SPYKER : You people should count yourselves lucky to be in this country. Look how much money the Government

60

spends on universities for you. And you don't even pay the tax. We white people have to pay taxes for *your* universities. You don't know when you're well off, man!

Haron lapsed into silence, gazing at the ceiling to display his contempt for Spyker's remarks.

GENIS : Please continue where you left off.

HARON : That's about all that happened in Cairo. I then went to London . . .

SPYKER : Hah! This is the interesting part. Now see that you stop lying and start telling the truth.

Haron proceeded to explain how he arrived in England, lived at an hotel, went on sight-seeing expeditions, visited distant relatives living in England and met friends.

GENIS : Tell me about this meeting with Mujaheed.

HARON : Well, I know Mujaheed. He was a Councillor here in Cape Town and is quite well known. I looked him up as an old friend after we had met at Friday prayers in the Regent's Park Mosque . . .

Spyker lost patience. 'Here, God! You're a priest and you lie like a prostitute. The last time you told me that you didn't meet Mujaheed. Why did you lie?'

Genis signalled Spyker to calm down. 'So what did you two talk about?' he asked Haron.

HARON : We talked about his studies and his family and I asked him about prospects for my daughter's education.

GENIS : Anything else?

HARON : He took me sight-seeing around London.

GENIS : Is that all?

HARON : Yes.

GENIS : Didn't you meet any of his terrorist friends?

HARON : Not that I know of.

GENIS : Let me jog your memory . . . (he mentions a few names). Didn't you meet any of these people?

HARON : No.

GENIS : It's remarkable how your memory fails you at convenient moments, isn't it? You are, of course, aware that Mujaheed and these other people are connected with the banned Pan-Africanist Congress?

HARON : I don't know about that. I've got nothing to do with the PAC.

61

Genis wanted further details about this visit to London, and Haron obliged, emphasizing the visits to relatives, the sightseeing tours and the journey home. Genis was patient and allowed him to talk freely.

GENIS : You did not happen to meet Canon Collins, did you?
HARON : No, I don't know this Canon Collins.
GENIS : No? Very interesting. Very interesting. Well, look, you can go and have your supper now. Sergeant, take the detainee back to his cell.

Spyker had been eagerly waiting for the signal to assail Haron with abuse, but the plan of campaign had been decided upon and the Major was sticking to it. He would have to content himself with the 'low-key' approach for the time being. This case was to be handled differently because of the lessons learnt in such cases as that of Ruth First.

It was now mid-afternoon. Viktor said that was enough for the day, he left the room.

Swanepoel sorted his notes, pinned them together, and tilted back his chair.

'You don't think that's a statement, do you?' he roared. . . . Swanepoel's face grew purple as he raged. The other detectives were now standing and watching me . . . Swanepoel went on the rampage again . . . The bombardment from Swanepoel split my bamboozlement wide open and it dropped from my head like a broken husk . . . Only now when I was to be taken back to Marshall Square, did Viktor reappear. That was the end of any statement from me I told him and others still in the room . . .

Once (Viktor) forgot himself and grumbled his peeve. 'Swanepoel spoilt it all', he said, and then stopped himself. How desperate they were for a statement and I would not give them one. (Ruth First: '117 Days')

Back in the horrible little cell. And once more the rattle of keys, the banging of gates, the crash of steel doors, the clatter of buckets. The magnificent diet of coffee and bread being served. Everybody dashing about. Opportunity to use the lavatory before lock-up. Tenants of every cell creating as much confusion as the warder would tolerate. Exchanging notes, information, tobacco, news, names. Haron did not have much chance. Inexperience. He accepted coffee. No bread. He asked the warder about his food from home. 'I'll see the sergeant.' No supper. Prayers. And then Spyker again. Not again! Yes, again! Spyker is a glutton for work! Back to the interrogation room. Who's this? Not Genis! Major? Captain? Lieutenant? Can't say. He's in mufti.

Interrogator began: 'Well, here we are, Imam Haron. Please sit down.'

Haron was concerned about his food and was feeling hungry. He decided it was best to make his complaint known without delay. 'I asked Major Genis about my food. He said it would be all right for my wife to bring it from home, but I have still received nothing. There must be some sort of hold-up at the charge-office.'

Interrogator raised his eyebrows and looked at Spyker.

Spyker made a helpless gesture. 'The Major said he would give instructions. Something must have gone wrong.' He spoke far too innocently.

'Never mind. Don't worry, Imam.' Interrogator dismissed the matter lightly. 'The Major will fix it up.'

'I had no supper last night and nothing to eat today, and I'm hungry,' complained Haron.

Interrogator was displeased with this start to the session. This 'Malay' priest wants to stand up for his rights too much, he thought. This wasn't a good sign.

'Can't you have some of the food from our kitchen until the matter is fixed up?' he asked. 'It's good food. The same as we eat.'

Spyker smirked. He knew the Imam's strength of feeling on the matter. Whether he accepted or not, it would be a little victory for them. Eat Christian food or starve. Meanwhile the inconvenience he was being caused would serve to emphasize that life in detention was not going to be a picnic.

'No. I only eat halal food,' said the Imam.

'I'm sorry, then I can't help you,' responded Interrogator. 'Please fix this problem up with the Major, Sergeant. Now, can we get on with this statement!

'Now let me see. Where were we?' hummed Interrogator. 'Oh, yes, here we are. You feel very strongly about the Group Areas Act and job reservation and such things, hey, Imam?'
HARON : Yes, I do.

INTERROGATOR : Well, all right. I don't mind a man having his opinions. Every man is entitled to his opinions. But the law is the law. We can't have people going around breaking the law!

HARON : I don't know about that. We don't have the vote, so what must we do?

SPYKER : It's best for you to answer questions instead of asking things like that. Have you been breaking the law?

INTERROGATOR : Yes, that's an interesting point arising out of your question: have you been breaking the law?

HARON : I don't know. Anyway, I have to uphold God's law.

INTERROGATOR : And if you think that the laws of our country are against God's law, you can break them? Is that right?

HARON : That's my duty!

INTERROGATOR : That's very interesting.

SPYKER : In other words you want to be prosecutor, judge and jury?

HARON : Just like you!

SPYKER : That's nonsense! You're talking shit. You've got no right to break the laws of the country!

INTERROGATOR : You must have quite a lot of money to go overseas so often. Where do you get all this money?

HARON : I save it. I've got a good job and I don't smoke or drink.

INTERROGATOR : How can you say you're oppressed, then? You not only have a good job and earn a lot of money, but you can even get a passport to go overseas!

HARON : Of course I'm oppressed. I have no say in the way my country is run. And I see injustice being done to my people. And there is poverty everywhere.

INTERROGATOR : Ugh, man, you're just imagining things. You have a nice family and a nice house that even I cannot afford. You're not oppressed, man; why do you want to get mixed up with kaffirs and terrorists? Why don't you just stick to religion and leave politics alone?

HARON : The way I look at it, religion *is* politics. My religion says that all men are created equal. This Government says that white supremacy is right. To accept that kind of thing would be a great sin for me. I believe in freedom, and having a nice house and a good job is not enough. It does not provide food for my soul.

INTERROGATOR : But we don't want to oppress anyone. The Government wants to keep races apart because living together creates friction. We believe in separate but equal rights for all. But the Bantu and people like you aren't ready for that yet. So the policy, like the Bantustan policy, has to be developed slowly. On the other hand, the trouble with many blacks, you know, is that they just want to marry our daughters!

Haron laughed. 'We are not asking to be your brother-in-law! We want to be your brothers. But don't talk to me about separate and equal; you know as well as I do that it has long ago been proved to be a farce.'

SPYKER : Man, if the kaffirs get half a chance, they'll kill all us whites, and you Coloureds too. That's why we must keep them in their place.

HARON : The Government is sowing the seeds of discontent. Oppression breeds resistance, man. There is an Arabic expression: 'He who lights a fire gets burnt'.

Interrogator straightened himself and looked pleased. 'Just so. Just so. And that's why you are here. You have lit a fire and you are getting burnt.'

Haron felt tired and very hungry. He did not feel like continuing this discussion. It was all so futile. How could he think anything he said would persuade or impress these two? He lapsed into silence.

Interrogator peered at the file in front of him, turning a page occasionally. Spyker sat quietly drumming his ball-point on his notebook, chin in his hand, staring at Haron through half-closed eyes. He was also tired. And he was annoyed at the 'soft' line being taken with Haron.

INTERROGATOR : This Ibadurahman Study Circle: you are the leader, and we have reason to believe that it is a subversive organization. But you, needless to say, would deny that. What precisely *is* the purpose of this organization?

HARON : The Ibadurahman Study Circle has been in existence for a long time. It is a study group, not a political party. It examines society against an Islamic background.

Your men have raided my mosque often enough to investigate it, and they never found anything wrong.

INTERROGATOR : Is it the purpose of this study circle, as you call it, to get scholarships for people to go and study overseas?

HARON : No. It is just a study group.

INTERROGATOR : How are people to be recruited to take up all these scholarships you are organizing all over the place?

HARON : I will select the students.

INTERROGATOR : How are you going to find the students? How will you know who is interested and decide upon their suitability?

HARON : I will get to know about students because of my connection with the Ibadurahman Study Circle and with the madressas of the various mosques, as well as my contact with the other schools and teachers. Anyway, it is my hope that a committee of interested people could eventually be established to go into questions of selection.

INTERROGATOR : How are you to get the money to send these students overseas?

HARON : Everything is not finished yet.

INTERROGATOR : Two years and things are not finalized yet? Are you sure that you have actually been trying to get *educational* scholarships?

HARON : There have been difficulties.

INTERROGATOR : In other words, you have not sent any students overseas yet?

HARON : That's right.

INTERROGATOR : Now, about this welfare work you do. Tell me about that.

Haron was very tired now. Hunger pains gnawed at his stomach. He slumped in his chair and volunteered a mumble. 'I'm tired. I've told you people about my welfare work many times.'

SPYKER : Tired? Well, I'm tired of listening to all these lies.

INTERROGATOR : Just tell me about this welfare work again. I want to be satisfied about it. Get it clear in my head, you know?

The exhausted Haron then had to recount once more his obligations under Islam, his unhappiness about suffering, his fund-raising activities to raise money for the poor.

INTERROGATOR : It seems that you make a point of supporting the families of enemies of the State?

HARON : I have helped some of the families of men who are in prison.

INTERROGATOR : But not the families of criminals like thieves and murderers and so on?

HARON : Sometimes.

INTERROGATOR : But mainly so-called political prisoners?

HARON : I don't ask what the man has done.

INTERROGATOR : Where do you keep your records of help given to people?

HARON : I don't keep records.

INTERROGATOR : That's very careless, isn't it? You know, any registered charity which gets money from the public through fund-raising like you do is required to keep proper records.

HARON : My efforts are very small and informal. My mosque and all the mosques have always helped people on a completely informal basis.

INTERROGATOR : Have you ever helped people by way of paying their legal fees in court cases?

HARON : It is possible, but I can't remember.

INTERROGATOR : Would you have helped terrorists with their legal fees?

HARON : Definitely not. I would remember some thing like that, and I have no recollection of helping anyone in such a case.

INTERROGATOR : Well, we will carefully consider everything you have told us and the answers you have given to our questions. You don't seem to have added much to what you have told us previously but we will be fair. Major Genis will see you tomorrow about it. I think that will do for tonight. You can return to your cell now.

Haron collapsed with relief on his thin bed of blankets which did so little to relieve the hardness of the concrete floor. The whole day's interrogation and talking and concentration had drained his strength. His stomach felt knotted with strain and hunger. After a few moments of relaxation, he still had to say his prayers and make up for those he had missed. Despite the discomfort and the worry, he soon fell asleep. He desperately needed to sleep.

Chapter Seven

Interrogation: Intensification

Inquest:

GENIS : *It happens like this. When I come on duty at eight in the morning, then I start questioning the man. I talk to him until twelve-thirty, one p.m. Then I let him eat and we come back at one-thirty, a quarter to two, and resume questioning until four-thirty or five or as long as the specific case . . .*

COOPER : *Was it ever later than four-thirty or five that you questioned the deceased?*

GENIS : *Yes, sometimes we started later. This happened when we came on duty at four-thirty . . . Yes, I believe we did . . . one occasion till midnight.*

(Genis carefully refers only to himself, neglecting to mention what happened before he came on late duty or after he went off early duty).

Early in the morning Haron is once more shaken awake by the chorus of rattling, shouting, banging, clanging, clattering noises. Breakfast is served: coffee and bread. The lavatory is waiting. The wash-basin is free. He has said his 'Subuh' but it is still dark. He had made a pledge to fast during the day and have one meal at night. But he has not eaten now for nearly two days because his food has not arrived from home and he is unable to eat 'Christian' food. What should he do? Make a hunger strike of it? Or should he starve himself? Or should he have some coffee and bread?

He decided against a hunger strike. The great Boerenasie would either simply let him starve to death without batting an eyelid or would force him to eat with all the brutality at their command. Hunger strikes are efficacious only against civilized opposition. Simply go without food until he received meals from home? Well, he needed his strength for the contest with his captors, but if there was no alternative he would simply have to stay without food. But bread *was* an alternative. It was vegetable. He decided to replenish his strength as far as this was possible with bread and coffee. He needed that bread! One must show some flexibility.

Eight o'clock was not long gone when a rattle-clatter-bang announced the arrival of Genis and a colleague. The hard-working Spyker was having a rest this morning, but Haron was allowed no such luxury.

Seated once more in the interrogation room, Haron took careful note of Genis's new companion. Was there something about the eyes? Yes, it could be the infamous Andries, brother of Spyker. Haron had seen him before, but without taking particular notice of him. Mean, ugly-looking type.

GENIS : Imam Haron, this statement you have been making these last two days: is this all you can tell us?

HARON : Yes, as far as I can remember.

GENIS : Well, it is not good enough, I'm afraid. I have compared it with the information in our files and it turns out to be a lot of nonsense. I'm surprised at you, thinking you can get us to believe it. Really, you should not let your pride stand in your way, you know. You've been caught out; admit it and make a clean breast of things. After all, pride goes before a fall, doesn't it? You know your family is very anxious about you and I have told them that if only you weren't so proud and stubborn by now you could have been reunited with them. Won't you reconsider your attitude?

HARON : So you've spoken with my family, Major. Then you must know about my food. I haven't had any yet.

GENIS : Haven't you? Good gracious. I told Sergeant van Wyk to get it fixed up. He must have slipped up. Are you sure your wife brought food for you?

70

HARON :   No doubt about it. She wouldn't slip up on a thing like that.

GENIS :   Yes? Now look, Andries, will you get the Imam's food fixed up with the charge-office?

ANDRIES :   Ja, Majoor!

GENIS :   Now that's settled, can we get on, Mr Haron? Where was I? Oh, yes. I don't want to be harsh, you understand, but this statement of yours just is not good enough. Not to put too fine a point on it, it's filled with lies. And even between the lies there are enormous gaps. I would like you to rectify these lies and fill in the gaps.

Andries, his eyes mere slits, gazed threateningly at Haron. He remained silent. He was being kept on a leash but was chafing under the restraint. Haron's cherished hopes lay dashed: they just wouldn't accept the story. He did not speak, waiting for the inevitable flood of questions.

GENIS :   Just to refresh your memory. You admitted to associating with a certain terrorist in Mecca in 1966. Together with this terrorist you distributed leaflets harmful to South Africa and calculated to embarrass the government. By a strange coincidence your memory fails you when it comes to remembering the names of people who helped you carry out these activities. Then suddenly you became very wealthy and you found it possible to travel with your wife, first to Egypt and then to England. In Cairo you became so important that you found yourself being invited to State functions. And this you explained by saying that you had good friends there. You deny any association with terrorists while you were in Cairo, which I don't accept for one moment. In London you became closely associated with another known terrorist – an intimate friend of your previous contact, and both connected with the PAC. But your memory fails you once more when it comes to remembering other names. Very conveniently, it was these same terrorists you visited once more in 1968, ostensibly to arrange for your daughter's education. I must say, I am shocked that a man like you will use his daughter to cover up his own misdeeds. Well, once more I just don't believe that this was the real reason for your so-called holiday in 1968. You are a man who has always taken an interest in

71

welfare work and I respect you for that. But, once more, I believe you used this welfare work as a cover for illegal activities. You almost went as far as to say that your main welfare work was to help the families of terrorists. You deny that you assisted with the payment of legal fees in political cases. But we will go into that later. Meanwhile I can tell you that your cover is blown. We have been aware of your activities all along, so don't run away with the idea that you have been putting us off the scent. Let me assure you, you will be kept in detention until you tell us the whole truth! Now, are you going to talk?

Haron remained externally composed but his brain was racing, how much did they know? Well let them blow hot and cold, he was not going to put a noose around his own neck. Their tale about letting him go if he talked didn't fool him for a minute. They had always been dishonest, mean and vengeful. And they had blood on their hands already.

HARON : You're mistaken, Major, I've told you everything. And I haven't engaged in unlawful activities. The people I met abroad are people I've known for a long time. I have known people from both ANC and PAC. Nobody gave me instructions, and if they tried I would have refused. The only thing you have against me is what I did in Mecca. But what I said there is no more than I have said from the mimbar many times.

GENIS : You may have known people who were involved with PAC and ANC for a long time – and that is not to your credit. But getting involved in their activities is a far more serious matter. Furthermore, you have made a most damaging confession: you have admitted that if you are not happy with laws of the land you feel you can break them. So it is easy to understand how you could go and get yourself involved in illegal activities. I believe you did just that.

HARON : No, I did not. I know nothing about ANC and PAC activities.

GENIS : Now you are not going to deny that you were involved with the Coloured People's Congress, are you?

HARON : No, but the Coloured People's Congress was not banned. And I was not actually a member.

GENIS : Don't try to mislead me with technicalities. Anyway,

72

it did not stop you from helping Gamat to break the law by carrying on with its activities.

HARON : That was his business, not mine.

GENIS : And it did not stop you from actively associating with him and others after the Coloured People's Congress was dissolved and joined the PAC. Our information is that you were in fact carrying out PAC activities from that time on.

HARON : No, I was not. I did not know they had joined PAC. After all, you did not arrest anyone.

GENIS : We have our reasons, Imam. We have our reasons. Anyway, let's not play ducks and drakes with each other. Let me show you this. Here I have a copy of the leaflet you distributed in Mecca. You will note that we collect our evidence in cases like this. And here I have a report of your meeting with Leballo of PAC in Cairo in 1966. You have kept quiet about that meeting so far, but here we have the hard evidence! Now perhaps you will tell me about this meeting?

HARON : Leballo? . . . I met Leballo? No, I didn't meet Leballo!

GENIS : I say you did. And here is the proof!

HARON : Your informers are mistaken.

GENIS : Informants, not informers, if you don't mind! Anyway, there's no use denying it. You might as well tell us about it. You see, we have a very strong intelligence network overseas and there is not a thing you have done that we don't know about.

Haron looked at the Major and his colleague in turn, but did not speak.

GENIS : You are going to tell us about it in the end, so you might as well do so now. It will save both your time and ours. Although, of course, we have all the time in the world and it's only yours you will be wasting.

HARON : I can't remember anything about meeting Leballo. I don't know what you're talking about.

GENIS : All right have it your own way. You must like to do things the hard way. It's nearly lunchtime. The sergeant will take you back to your cell.

Genis picked up his file and strode out of the room. Andries

73

snarled at Haron, 'You think you are clever, but we will break you, man. We'll break you! We have broken better men than you. So watch out!'

Haron ignored him. He returned to his cell.

Haron's letter of 8 May 1969: They had a file on me about both trips overseas, they mentioned your name and brother Abraham. I denied everything . . .
Haron's letter of 26 July 1969, smuggled out of Caledon Square: Your instructions to me for students etc. They have it on paper . . . My meetings in Cairo etc. is on paper at the S/B . . . They say that their overseas intelligence is powerful . . .

Genis and company had their lunch and afterwards went to the office of their chief, the colonel in charge of their department, to confer on the Haron case. They made no move to inform Haron that he would not be required for interrogation that afternoon. It was not part of the scheme of things to relieve the detainee of uncertainty: he could sit in his cell and worry and wonder about what would come next. Haron had proved uncooperative, as had been expected, and it was now necessary to discuss his statement carefully in order to expose the inconsistencies and lies by comparing it with the information already in their files and setting the intelligence machine in motion to check up on things he had said. It was a convenient time to have this discussion because the following day, 31 May, was an important public holiday – Republic Day. No one intended working late or coming in over the weekend if it could be helped. They could make a fresh start on Haron on Monday.

On Republic Day all good Boers would be in church, at mass political rallies or recreation grounds, to celebrate the birth of the great Boer republic of South Africa. In the churches, the infamous 'political predikants' of the Dutch Reformed Church would be giving praise to God on high for the famous Boer victories and exhorting His 'chosen people' to be true to their mission on Earth – keeping the kaffir in his place. The mass rallies would celebrate with hysterical orgies of racialist tub-thumping, and declamations against the 'Communist menace', the 'black danger', the 'yellow peril', the 'English gutter press', etc., etc., etc. Everyone would go away rejuvenated, once more

74

to fight the great fight against a world of 'liberalistic' enemies. At the recreation grounds, those famous old Boer games of rugby and jukskei would inspire all to develop huge muscles and become six-feet-four-inch specimens of well-fed humanity, sure to impress any kaffir with the superiority of the white man. After these important events – the South African equivalent of the Nuremberg rallies of Hitler – everybody could return to normal life, convinced once more of the rectitude and righteousness of the Boerenasie. Such festivities were not to be missed by a political or Special Branch policeman.

Haron could spend his afternoon in prayer and quiet contemplation. But evening brought great activity and movement to the cells. It was Friday, time for the good old white South African custom of abusing and knocking about all available drunks who had the misfortune to fall into the clutches of that unique thing called South African law. It was late before the drunkards were settled for the night and their jack-booted tormentors had had enough of their sport.

Once more Haron wondered whether to accept the proffered two slices of brown bread at supper time. No, he had been assured that his food problem would be attended to, so there was no need. Once more he waited in vain. No food arrived and he had not accepted the food from the police station's kitchen. So he could look forward to another hungry night. He was angry. He was sure that his captors were enjoying themselves at his expense. 'Fock hom! hy kan kak!' (Fuck him! He can shit!) they were probably saying to each other. But they would not get the better of him. He would not give in to pressure.

Saturday turned out to be a day free from interrogation. The political police were having their brains washed, thumping their tubs and building their muscles. Haron too was allowed some fresh air, although in his case it was for only an hour. Still it was a great relief to get out of that little cupboard of a cell. At the time of the morning when he was escorted to the exercise yard, the sun was still all but blocked off by the high walls to which the chill of night still clung. It was late autumn and the cold of winter had not yet arrived, so the morning air was invigorating. In June the Cape always promised warm sunny days, even if interrupted by occasional winter rains, but the nights were cool and damp. Unfortunately, there was not much sun to be had in the little exercise yard, and none at all in the cupboard of a cell. The hour in the yard ended far too quickly with the slam of the cell door and the terrible clatter of the keys.

The afternoon stretched away ahead. From time to time the City Hall clock would announce the passing hours if one listened carefully. Haron had many memories he could dream about. There were memories of childhood, of Mecca, Cairo and London; memories of marriages and fatherhood. He could smile at the wonderful times he had had at marriage ceremonies he had conducted. The good-natured bartering over dowries, the wonderful hand-made bridal costumes, the colour and pomp of the parade of the bridal pair through the streets in the beautiful horse-drawn coach which the wealthier Muslims absolutely insisted on. It was remarkable, the way the Muslims had blended western and oriental customs to keep the traditions alive. The only place these days where one could see Christians using horse-drawn coaches was at the race-tracks where people who had won money would get drunk as lords and then go home in style. There was quite a traffic in these coaches at Kenilworth race-course on Saturday mornings and afternoons. He hoped his congregation were not gambling away their hard-earned money today. But there were some, of course . . .

How he had enjoyed the fuss and the eating, the jam tarts and coconut tarts at all the Islamic baptisms. Somehow his thoughts turned to food all the time. He was glad he had taken the bread that morning. It had tasted like the finest Muslim pastry despite being completely dry! He must complain about this food question. They had no right to withhold his food when they were not in a position to supply halal food. Man cannot live on two slices of dry bread and coffee alone!

Being the centre of attraction as the officiating Imam was quite a thing. The uninitiated always thought he was doing something wonderful and strange when he leaned forward and whispered in the little infant's ear. But it was only the Muezzin's call which he whispered to baptize the little thing. He was glad that the cirumcisions were done mainly by doctors or at the hospitals these days. Ritual made it necessary for the circumcision to be done but he had never had the heart for it. Of course some of the more conservative complained that this was not right, but then they complained about everything. But were circumcision and all the rest of the ritual really necessary? He wondered. It did serve to bind people more closely to their faith. On the other hand, a person's faith was something existing within, of which the rituals were only an outward show. However, as the Imam he must observe the rituals strictly.

The complaint about his food brought a positive and very welcome response. That was a good thing. It showed them that, although he was completely in their power, he would nonetheless press for proper treatment as far as he was able and the opportunity arose. It was right to show some fight, even in these conditions.

That evening Haron received a plate heaped with delicious food from home, and some sweetmeats and a change of clothing. He could now relax with a full stomach.

Inquest:
GENIS : *Because he was a follower of the Muhammadan · religion and had particular foods, he was allowed, a few days after his arrest, to receive food, eatables, fruit, etc. from his house.*

On Sunday, Haron's routine was much the same as it had been on Saturday. The eager defenders of the Boerenasie also needed their holidays. The only problems the detainees had to deal with were the confinement and the loneliness. Even the warders worked at finding nothing to do and rarely came to the cells. Now and again there would be some aggravation at having a parcel to deliver to someone or having to come and release a prisoner for whom bail or a fine had been paid. Otherwise, not much at all appeared to be going on.

No one told him to be quiet when he began whistling and singing quietly to himself. He loved the old 'liedjies' (ditties) of the Cape Coloureds, which the Muslims had done so much to preserve. There was 'Rosa' which was the best-loved and was sung with deep feeling on the most important occasions; but the most popular by far was the one about the nineteenth-century American steel-hulled ship *Alabama*. It had been among the first steel-hulled ships in the world and had stalked the Atlantic Ocean during the American Civil War. That war had been about the abolition of slavery, and was therefore meaningful to the Cape Coloureds, many of whom had been emancipated from slavery only thirty years before.

Daar Kom die Alabama
Die Alabama die kom
Oor die see-ee-ee-ee
Daar kom die Alabama . . .

(There comes the *Alabama*/The *Alabama* she comes/Over the sea-ea-ea-ea/There comes the *Alabama* . . .)

All in all, the weekend did not pass off too badly. Haron had now established some kind of routine. His food was being delivered as arranged and his plan – to fast during the day and take one meal at night – could therefore be pursued. The change of clothing once a week would assist his morale by keeping a point of contact, however tenuous, with his wife, family and friends, and the whole outside world. His sunrise and midnight prayers had been left relatively undisturbed by the vagaries of the interrogation sessions and these would be his main times for prayer. The other prayer times were subject to disturbance by the demands of his captors and he would have to fit these in as the opportunity arose, and make up later for any he missed. They were allowing him out for exercise in the mornings, but his experience had already shown this also could be interrupted for periods of interrogation. He would have to demand to be allowed to go to the yard at a later time if he lost the opportunity in the morning. He would also do press-ups and other exercises in his cell. Although it was small, he had now decided that he could walk up and down its length for a few miles. He was getting used to the noisy activity which broke out in the cells when bread and coffee was served, and he noted the friendliness and interest on the faces of the other prisoners. The possibility of making contact existed; the communal lavatory/wash-basin and the exercise yard, he concluded, were places where written messages could be left and exchanged. These possibilities needed to be explored, not least importantly because concocting schemes to outwit the warders and the police provided something to occupy the mind.

On Monday morning it became clear that the interrogators were trying a different tack. They did not accept his story and had made up their minds that the interrogation was going to

78

take too long. They made this clear to Haron and expressed the view that he was only wasting his own time, because in the end he would talk. Now they started not with his 'political pilgrimage' but much further back. He must tell his life story. They would apply their pressure from the time he was elected to be the Imam of his mosque, would commence detailed questioning from 1960 when his concern for the suffering in Langa and Nyanga and for the families of the detainees during the state of emergency was first noticed. Haron proceeded to drone out his story, interspersed with occasional questions from his tormentors. This is how it went on, day after day.

Once, a week after Haron's detention – on Wednesday, 4 June – the carefully laid plans to isolate him from all contact with his family and the world went awry. It was late afternoon, and it had been decided that as Haron was going to be in the cells a long time, his fingerprints must be taken. Spyker brought him down to a reception room on the ground floor. The corridor to the cells passed the door of this reception room and directly opposite was the door of the charge-office.

Spyker was methodical and not at all gentle about his work. He placed Haron's thumbs, every finger, palms and both sides of the hands on the black ink-pad and vigorously pressed them on the description form. Methodically he made the appropriate ticks relating to the detainee's physical and racial characteristics. As he pushed Haron to the measuring rod, under the slide, to take his height, Spyker could not resist temptation. With a self-satisfied smirk and a vicious little tug, he brought the slide, bang, down on Haron's head. 'Fife foot five!' he rapped out, with a vicious glint in his eyes as Haron cried out in pain and stood massaging his scalp. Just a taste of things to come, said the look on Spyker's face.

At that very moment, food and clothing were being brought to the charge-office for Haron by family friends, accompanied by his son Mohammed. The boy was desperately anxious to see his father and strayed into the passage-way leading to the cells. Someone had left the door of the corridor ajar so Mohammed just wandered through. A short way down the corridor was an open door and he saw a fez on a table in the room. Excitedly the boy called out, 'Daddy, Daddy! Are you there?'

Haron immediately recognized the voice and reacted swiftly:

79

'Mohammed, Mohammed! I am here. Tell Mummy I'm all right!' For a brief moment his isolation was broken . . .

Spyker also reacted quickly. Indeed, he reacted as though he had just been scalded. He rushed from the reception room in a towering rage, banging the door shut behind him as he went. He pushed the boy violently out of the corridor and slammed that door, just as the poor warder who had left it ajar appeared. Haron could afford to laugh at the shower of abuse to which the warder was subjected; everybody would know that all was well.

On 10 June, a fortnight after Haron was detained, some members of the Al Jaamia mosque entered the House of Parliament, which is situated next to the Cape Town Gardens at the top of the city's main thoroughfare, Adderley Street. At the reception desk they were given permits for the 'non-European' public gallery on the authority of the (white) United Party (white) Member of Parliament for the (white) constituency of Wynberg. They had approached this MP previously to introduce the question of their Imam's detention to Parliament. The visitors were shown to a small balcony directly above the Government benches.

Mrs Catherine Taylor, MP, had set down a series of questions to the Minister of Police on the arrest and detention of Abdulla Haron. While in general white Members of Parliament are resented by blacks, they are sometimes regarded as useful to get information concerning important public affairs from Cabinet Ministers at Parliamentary question times. Catherine Taylor established that Haron was indeed being detained 'since 28 May 1969, under section 6 of Act 83 of 1967' (The Terrorism Act); that the police were in no position to commence proceedings against Haron or anyone else because 'this depends on the evidence available on completion of the investigation'; that no request for reading matter had been received from Haron (according to the police).

On 13 June, the same MP once more questioned the Minister of Police about Abdulla Haron. On this occasion the Minister pleaded that it was 'not in the public interest' to disclose where Haron was being detained or why he had not been released.

Haron learned from the warder on duty in the cells that questions had been asked about him in Parliament. The warder, of course, broke the rules by conversing with Haron, but he could hardly contain himself. It was not every day that he was privileged to guard a 'Malay' priest, and these people were reputed to possess supernatural powers! The poor Boer had been fed from birth on a beggar's diet of rigid Calvinism which only served to heighten his astonishing superstitiousness. Now it turned out that Haron was important enough for questions to be asked in Parliament about him. The incident served to break the ice and surreptitious words were exchanged from time to time thereafter.

The incident with Mohammed, his son, and the questions about him in Parliament, helped to sustain Haron in his isolation. He might be entirely in the power of the State and its agencies and be locked away from society; but he was not lost and forgotten. But he was thrown back upon his own inner strength in order to keep his sanity and his resolution. This inner strength derived from his deep religious commitment. He recited verses from the Koran almost continuously. He was indifferent to the visits of magistrates. South Africa's magistrates – all white – had rarely been known to be anything other than willing tools in the implementation of the most tyrannical laws. The day of his longed-for release would be determined by the wish of Allah, and it was to Allah that he looked for protection, not to the lackeys of the racist state.

By the end of June the battery of interrogators headed by Major Genis had gone over Haron's story repeatedly, sifting every detail carefully and presenting to him the evidence of his misdemeanours. They had a copy of the leaflet that he had distributed in Mecca and reports of his association with Abraham. These he had long ago acknowledged and had accepted sole responsibility for. There was the report of his meeting with Leballo of the PAC in Cairo and also one of his visits to the Cairo offices of the PAC. These he denied. He denied the charge that he had received instructions from abroad in connection with the Ibadurahman Study Circle. His interrogators were obliged to give him still more convincing evidence of the extent of their knowledge of his activities, to impress on him thereby the futility of his withholding information. Therefore Genis put to Abdulla Haron the full allegations against him.

Inquest – *affidavit of Major Genis:*
The deceased was detained because over the years reliable information was obtained that he –

(a) *had instructions to recruit students who were going to study overseas and young Muslims who were going as pilgrims to Mecca and had passports, for terrorist training in China;*

(b) *was involved with the pursuit of the aims and objects of the banned PAC organization and with recruiting members for it;*

(c) *received thousands of rands from overseas through different banks for unlawful purposes;*

(d) *contravened currency regulations by illegally taking out of the Republic of South Africa thousands of rands for, amongst other things, political exiles overseas;*

(e) *visited the terrorist headquarters in Cairo and made contact with members of the PAC movement;*

(f) *had meetings overseas with known terrorists and accepted instructions from them;*

(g) *continuously communicated in secret with terrorists overseas.*

Abdulla Haron's denials were countered by presenting him with his bank statements showing that in the period 1966/67/68 he had received R4000 (about $4000) from overseas. The police had frozen his bank accounts. They then shattered him by giving him an account of everything that was discussed at meetings he had attended in London. They showed him reports of his meeting with Canon Collins. They further showed him that certain associates of his had in fact been passing information on to them. He was reduced to despair on being presented with a letter which should have been sent abroad by a colleague but which this colleague had asked another person to write. That person had brought the letter to the police. They had a complete list of code names used.

Haron's letter of 26 July to Mujaheed: Everything we discussed at ——'s house in 1966 is an open secret with the S/B. —— is well liked by the S/B. They told me he is a softie . . . They also mention the name of ——. But I don't know her. I presume she and —— are on good sexy terms? . . . You did send the money but it is being frozen by the S/B . . . I told —— to get in touch with you . . . According to the S/B this letter was written to you. But —— did not write it. He had someone to write it and that person brought the letter to them, S/B.

Haron now saw the subtlety of his original interrogation: he had been invited to make small admissions on the basis of information they put to him; but they had further information which would be released little by little to elicit more and more admissions until the whole story was out. From the meeting with Leballo in Cairo, he would be led to admitting that he had attended meetings of the PAC there, and then that they had discussed organizational work. From admissions of meeting members of the PAC and attending their meetings, he would be led to the admission that he had accepted their instructions. After admitting that he had met Canon Collins, he would be presented with bank statements proving that he had received money from overseas; then he would be given the names of one or two people whom he had assisted financially, a fact he would be forced to concede. He had cover stories prepared which from time to time he offered his interrogators but, once he started to offer admissions and explanations, the dialogue developed a momentum of its own.

HARON : I admit that I went to the PAC office in Cairo but this was only to get their help to arrange an appointment with Mr Fayek, the Minister of National Guidance. I was very anxious to arrange for students to go to Egypt, not only because it would be good for their education but also because it would help them to remain within the fold of Islam. I felt it would be better to get the help of an organization like PAC or ANC to make such an appointment. They asked me about things in South Africa when I went to their office, but that was all. Later I met Leballo briefly at the reception for the Iraqi Prime Minister. Mr Fayek definitely invited me himself. I did not talk to Leballo on that occasion. We just said hello to one another.

GENIS : Why did you lie about this previously?

HARON : I was afraid that it would be held against me if I admitted it. Although I see no harm in simply getting their help with scholarships. I meant no harm.

GENIS : No? Well, now that one lie has been exposed it would be reasonable to infer, wouldn't it, that there are others awaiting similar exposure? I suggest that the same thing happened in London. You met various enemies of South Africa there.

HARON :   Well, Mujaheed introduced me to some of his friends and we talked about various things. They knew that I do welfare work and so we discussed Defence and Aid which is banned but I never agreed to work for them.

GENIS :   Come on, Imam Haron, you don't expect me to believe that. I've shown you the proof – your own bank statements. You received R4000 from overseas. Where did that money come from if not from the Canon and/or The anti-apartheid movement?

HARON :   No, I have no dealings with them. That money was donated by the London Muslim Welfare Association for me to continue my missionary and welfare work in Langa and Nyanga and Guguleta and for the school I established for Muslim education in Bonteheuvel.

GENIS :   God, fathers, man! When are you going to make up your mind to tell the truth? I'm sure this London Muslim Welfare Association is just a fictitious organization you have sucked out of your thumb. But we will check it out. Now, I want a list of the people to whom you gave this money!

HARON :   I used some of the money to give to people, but most of it I gave to schools, churches, mosques.

GENIS :   Name them!

HARON :   I can't remember.

GENIS :   You will have to remember or we will *make* you remember! Are you sure you would not prefer to do so now?

HARON :   I can't remember because I gave the money to anyone I thought was in need. I did not keep a list.

GENIS :   Our information is different. We have definite information, for example, that you gave certain people in Port Elizabeth money. In other words, you went 500 miles away, to give money to terrorists. We want this information, Haron, and you are going to give us that list, come what may!

Haron said nothing. There was a definite hardening in the attitude of the Major. His colleagues were all becoming more impatient and threatening as the month went on. It was clear to Haron that they were determined to put together a cast-iron case against him on the basis of his own admissions and thus build up a confession. But they also wanted names so that they could intimidate people into giving evidence against him. He was not prepared to give them any names.

GENIS : We have detained certain of the members of your Ibadurahman Study Circle and they have made certain admissions about your and this group's Poqo (PAC) activity. I want to know how many and who have been sent abroad for guerilla training and I want the names of the PAC people in your cells.

Haron was nearly overcome but managed to hide his feelings. The Major had just told a lie! Haron had received the information that certain youths had been detained and released again, and that they had told the police nothing. He had complete confidence in these youths. The Major's lie meant that he was on uncertain ground; he was not sure of his facts.

He said, 'The boys can't tell you what they don't know, Major, because there is nothing to tell. Nobody has been sent overseas for guerilla training and I am not involved with any Poqo activities.'

Genis's patience was at an end and he made this obvious. His colleagues were angry. They had had enough of this stonewalling and they were determined to nail Haron come hell, or high water. It was becoming clear that they would be treated to one lie after another but get no nearer to a single name which they could use against him. Naturally, they could not expose their agents who had provided their initial information from overseas. It was imperative to obtain a confession from Haron. They retired to confer and decided that the time had come to end their patient interrogation and resort to physical torture. The psychological torture and sensory deprivation of solitary confinement, coupled with the gruelling interrogation, were proving insufficient. This man would spend his whole life in solitary confinement and still not talk. They had accepted this possibility right from the outset. The time to 'break' him physically had now arrived.

Chapter Eight

Torture

On Monday, 23 June, the magistrate arrived bright and early for his fortnightly visit. He was less formal than on the previous occasion, smiled and noted that Abdulla Haron gave a clear reply to his question asking whether he was all right. With a 'hail-fellow-well-met' air carefully prepared to hide the perfunctoriness and pointlessness of it all, the magistrate then breezed out of the cell again. Genis, who had been hovering in the doorway, locked up and trotted along behind. Both were relieved that this particular sop to public opinion was out of the way. The magistrate was aware that questions had been asked in Parliament and was anxious to ensure that the formalities were respected. Genis, also very much aware of the parliamentary questions, was feeling the pressure to make headway with the investigation. With the formality of the magistrate's visit out of the way, he could now proceed to apply that pressure to Haron.

At his next interrogation Haron found Genis and Spyker accompanied by an intimidating crowd of the pride of the S.B. Questions were shot at Haron from all angles, but the demeanour of the interrogators remained relaxed. Haron was made to go through his story again via a question-and-answer process.

Finally, Genis gathered his papers together. 'That will be enough for today, I think,' he remarked, and with a satisfied smile to Haron got up and strode from the room. The gathered bully-boys observed Haron silently for a moment. He looked at the various faces, wondering uncertainly what was going on. Suddenly Spyker roared: 'Pig! You dirty stinking, lying, lump of shit! Who the fucking hell do you think you're leading up the garden path?'

Another grabbed Haron by his lapels, lifted him bodily off the chair and threw him against the wall. 'You Malay bastard!' he bellowed. 'We'll boil you in pork-fat and make you eat pig-shit! You black swine!'

Abuse and vilification such as he had never dreamed possible were heaped upon the little Imam, bending him double in a cringing lump against the wall. So venomous and painful was the verbal battery that Haron felt himself ducking and weaving and flailing his arms about to ward off the airy blasts. They prodded and pushed him and occasionally smacked him. Then, having worked themselves to a frenzy of animal fury, they suddenly withdrew, glowering, fists clenched, at the cringing frightened little man.

'Undress!' screamed Spyker at the top of his voice.

'What?' stammered the shocked Haron.

'Undress, damn you!' came a chorus of bellows, roars and shrieks from the gathered throng.

'You're not here to ask questions, you terrorist bastard,' screamed Spyker. 'You do as you're told. Put your clothes over there!'

Like a pack of hungry wolves the crowd of policemen pressed around the Imam, pushing, jostling and jabbing him as uncertainly he started to undress.

'Faster! Faster! You're not in a hotel!' the roars beat at his ears.

'The pork-fat is boiling!'

'We told you we would break you!'

'The time has come!'

'Now we'll make you talk!'

Haron was finally bare. Shrieks of laughter resounded around the room. Lewd and abusive jokes flew about his head, and suddenly fists were raining down upon it. And onto his stomach and his chest. He was flung about the room from one tormentor to another. When he fell, huge boots thudded into his body, then he was pulled to his feet and flung against the wall. This went on for some time until Haron collapsed in a heap, almost unconscious and unable to stand. He was then propped against the wall and slapped into consciousness.

Inquest into death of Looksmart Solwandle (1963): Isaac Tlale – I was told to undress . . . I did . . . I was handcuffed, there were two chairs which were joined together, I was asked to sit on two chairs . . . in between my knees they inserted a broom handle, thick . . . above my arms and below my knees . . . my head was covered with a bag. (Ruth First: '117 days').
Sworn Statement – Belinda Martin (1975): *The policemen told the two women to rough me up to give me a taste of the treatment I was to get from them. I was left alone with the two women. They stripped all my clothes off me. I was handcuffed by my hands and feet. Then they beat me. They hit me with their hands and fists.*

The Authors were personally informed by Ahmed Osman (90-day detainee, 1963) that during his brief interrogation he had been required to undress.

Inquest into the death of Steve Biko (1977): Biko was kept in a state of nudity for the entire period of his brief detention until his death. In this state, and mortally injured, he was transported 700 miles from Port Elizabeth to Pretoria. He was kept shackled, hand and foot, all the time.

Haron's whole body ached and he felt completely disorientated. On the left side of his chest he felt a terrible pain. One of his ribs was broken. He groaned with pain and anguish and complained about the broken rib. Gales of laughter, self-satisfied mockery and abuse for their prisoner poured from the crowd of torturers.

One walked up to him and prodded his chest. He shrieked with pain and collapsed on the floor. He was propped up once more.

'Talk!' bellowed Spyker.

Questions were shot at him from all sides. Hour after hour. Some of the torturers left, to be replaced by a new shift. When no answer was forthcoming or an answer he gave failed to satisfy them, one of the torturers would go up to Haron and renew the physical assault upon him.

'You won't get away with this,' moaned the desperate Haron. 'I'll report this to the magistrate and bring charges against the lot of you!'

'The magistrate!' howled the pack, falling about with laughter, 'You saw the magistrate on Monday and he won't be here for another two weeks.'

'If you complain, it will only be worse for you!' they threatened. 'Then we'll really fix you up!'

'If that magistrate tries to make trouble, we will lock him up too,' retorted another. 'We've got all the powers we need! You've got no way out!'

Haron stood, groaning with pain, feeling utterly humiliated, utterly helpless and utterly vulnerable. These men had the power of life and death over him. There was no redress and nowhere he could turn for help. Their knowledge of his activities was all but complete. They simply required corroboration, a few details and a confession. It was impossible and pointless to hold out against such strength. He might as well talk, since it would add nothing to what they already knew.

'Get me a doctor,' begged Haron, 'then I will talk.'

'You go and get bloody well fucked!' came the answer. 'You talk, and *then* we will get a doctor, you black filth.'

They returned him to his cell.

The following day it was agreed: he would make another statement and then they would see that he got medical attention.

Genis was now sent for. 'Ah! Imam Haron,' smiled Genis in his most friendly manner, 'I understand you have finally come to your senses and are now prepared to tell the truth. That's fine. Let us proceed then.'

And so Haron started to confess to some of the events and discussions in Cairo and London. As he told the story – carefully but with the most natural casualness he was capable of – he implicated all those who were in exile, beyond the reach of the State, but no one who remained in South Africa. He totally denied that the Ibadurahman Study Circle was in any way involved and took complete responsibility for all its activities.

Genis and his companions were quite satisfied with their work, but one blatant flaw did not escape their notice: not a single person was named who could be apprehended and terrorized into giving evidence against Haron in a public court of law. He also continued to insist that the monies he had received from overseas had been given to various mosques, churches and schools, and that he had used some for himself. He managed to protect the poor families of political prisoners in this way. Haron could name no one who had gone abroad for education or guerilla training.

Genis felt that the back of his resistance had been broken and that all this additional information would be forthcoming in due course. The interrogation and battering had taken all week.

It was now late on Friday and it was agreed that Haron would be allowed to see a doctor – a State district surgeon – the next day, Saturday. Genis blandly denied that he could have been tortured but was concerned that his rib might be broken and felt that this act might assist in his role as the 'sympathetic' interrogator.

Haron's letter of 26th July: The S/B want information out of me: (1) who are those working with me – I took everything on my own. I told them I am alone . . . (2) . . . they want to know who are the recipients of funds. I told them that I gave the money to schools, churches and mosques and I used some for myself . . .

Inquest:

van Wyk : *The deceased declared that he had used a large part of the money to build his house – he bought building material and other items connected with the building of his house. He gave some donations. He held parties for the Black Sash* and the rest of the money he naturally used for the purposes which I have stated i.e. the payment of fares etc. . . . we know how some of the money was spent, as to other parts we were unable to find out.*

The following day, Saturday 29 June, Haron was fetched from his cell and Major Genis and Captain E. J. J. Geldenhuys took him to the District Surgeon at Bellville which is about ten miles from Caledon Square. There were four District Surgeons serving the Cape Peninsula and, although it was a weekend, these men were on call if required. But the policemen preferred to take him ten miles away because they knew the doctor they were going to

* A white women's organization opposed to apartheid.

see could be trusted. This man, Dr Viviers, had a policy which commended him to dedicated political policemen: he 'never questioned political prisoners too precisely'.

Haron was in great pain and complained to Viviers particularly of the pain on the left side of his chest where he unquestionably had a broken rib. Viviers very cooperatively found no marks or bruises and could not establish through clinical examination that there was any injury to the ribs, pleura or lungs. He was fully aware that it was difficult to detect broken or cracked ribs without X-rays but 'surmised that the pain originated from the muscles in between the ribs'. Genis and Geldenhuys had been careful to advise the doctor that Haron was a political prisoner, and Viviers therefore did not question him about his injury. (Strangely Viviers was to remember, almost a year later and despite an absence of written records and a chilling lapse of memory in other respects, that the 'painful spot' was definitely on the left side, and not the right side, of the chest.) Haron's protestations were to no avail. He was sent packing with a few analgen pain-killing tablets.

Genis and Geldenhuys were delighted and drove the point home to Haron as they drove back to Caledon Square. 'You see, Haron, we have you completely in our power. Even the doctors cooperate with us! But when you have completed your statement and signed it, we will see that you get the best treatment available. We don't want to be hard. Only, you must cooperate, you see.'

Inquest:

DR VIVIERS :   *During the latter part of June 1969, Captain*
E. J. J. Geldenhuys and another detective brought a political
prisoner to my consulting room . . . I was advised that he was
a political prisoner and my policy is not to question them too
precisely . . . Well, look, if he told me . . . he said – it was
an injury . . . but I did not ask him, and I noticed that he
was not willing to talk.

John Shlapobersky (The Observer, *23 August 1970): I was*
taken to see a district surgeon who gave me an extremely
thorough examination and asked me if I had any relapse of my
jaundice. I said no, but tried to tell him how ill I felt after a night

92

on a brick. He was not interested, told me it was none of his business, and turning to Swanepoel said: 'Daar is niks verkeerd met hom nie – ry hom!' (There is nothing wrong with him – ride him!).

The fact that Haron had complained of the barbarous assault to which he had been subjected infuriated Spyker and his colleagues. They were full of threats as to the dire consequences which would result if he complained again. But Haron was not beaten. He brooded but remained determined that he would expose their behaviour. He also remained determined that there were limits to the information he was prepared to give his interrogators. He was not 'broken'.

A couple of days were absorbed by further questioning while the interrogators made notes, and by 2 July they were ready to get down to the serious business of preparing the statement for his signature. To remedy the gaps, policemen were sent out to investigate leads in order to obtain names and check on how money had been received and disbursed. Haron was presented with a ball-point and paper and invited to write down everything about himself. It was believed that in this way he would give more away about his activities than he had under interrogation. While Spyker worked from his notes, Haron sat writing. Spyker occasionally left his desk to peep over Haron's shoulder and read what he was writing; he would spur him on with some helpful abuse and the odd curse. Meanwhile two young members of Haron's congregation were detained and interrogated to check Haron's story.

By the first weekend of July, it became clear that the whole story had not been revealed. Spyker was very angry and decided to consult with Major Genis about what was to be done. Haron was clearly not broken, and further steps were necessary. Unfortunately the visit of the magistrate was due that Monday and if Haron complained, the magistrate could not be entirely relied upon to be as cooperative as Dr Viviers had been. It was thereupon decided that Haron should be taught a further 'lesson' and be terrorized into not complaining to the magistrate. But Spyker was too closely involved with the case and would therefore take the weekend off. The lesson could perhaps be given by Andries and some others.

The teachers of the lesson to Haron that weekend erred on the side of enthusiasm. So eager were they to get at the Imam that they could not wait to get him to their interrogation room; they started on him right in his cell. The thuds of blows and shrieks of pain rang through the whole cell-block as the muscle-men got to work. 'Ahad! Ahad!' wailed Haron as the blows rained down, and he called out prayers to Allah as the beating-up proceeded. But the thugs had been instructed not to go too far: he simply had to be terrorized; further information must be obtained and no complaints were to be made to the magistrate. For the prisoners in the other cells, the shrieks and prayers of the man in cell 164 made it a harrowing weekend.*

Much to the annoyance of the police, Haron did complain to the magistrate about his chest pains on Monday, 7 July. The magistrate was concerned but not overly so and suggested to Genis that medical attention was necessary.

'You should not have done that,' Genis said to Haron after the magistrate left. 'I told you that you could have the best treatment available when your statement is completed and signed.'

'Your men beat me up,' said Haron, 'I'm in pain and I need a doctor now.'

'Well, you won't get one until your statement is finished!' barked Genis.

'But, the magistrate said . . .' began Haron.

'To hell with what the magistrate said,' Genis interrupted. 'The magistrate does not run the Security Branch; you'll get medical attention when I say so.'

The 'sympathetic' interrogator succeeded in upsetting Haron quite considerably; but Spyker also was concerned, knowing his own record of brutality, what the consequences for him of a formal complaint might be. 'How will we explain it?' he asked Genis.

Glaring at Haron, Genis angrily suggested, 'We'll let him see a doctor when he has finished his statement. Meanwhile we will say that we took him to Dr Viviers today. That should fix up everything.'

* The Authors have been informed that prisoners on remand in the cells heard the beating, shouting and praying.

Inquest (1):

COOPER : *During that period [2 to 11 July] was he [Haron] at any stage taken to a doctor because of his pains?*

VAN WYK : *Not as far as I can recall because I remember that I was busy daily, from eight in the morning to one-thirty and again from two-thirty to five p.m. writing his statement . . . I do not recall that, during this time, he saw a doctor at any stage!!*

Inquest (2):

COOPER (summing up) : *My submission is that van Wyk's denial is unacceptable. That even if his denial is acceptable, the inescapable inference to be drawn from Haron's failure to complain to van Wyk, is that van Wyk committed, or was a party to, or had knowledge of, an assault which was the cause of Haron's pain . . . My submission is that taking these circumstances cumulatively, the only reasonable inference that can be drawn is that round about this time Haron had been assaulted on one or more occasions.*

On Wednesday, 10 July, the 43-page statement by Haron was complete. Spyker only wished to have it carefully considered for final approval by Major Genis, so that Haron could sign it the next day. Genis thereupon agreed that Haron could be taken for medical attention to the district surgeon in Cape Town.

Genis and Geldenhuys discovered that they need not have troubled to take Haron all the way to Bellville to see Dr Viviers on the previous occasion; although a Boer doctor was always preferable, right there in the city there turned out to be a district surgeon with the all-too-English name of D'Arcy Charles Gosling. Dr Gosling examined Haron for between ten and fifteen minutes without, as became clearer at the inquest, putting a single question to him. Haron was by now very wary of these 'public servants'. Viviers had ignored him, the magistrate had adopted the position that everything was all right, and Genis had treated the magistrate with contempt. Apparently everyone felt it necessary to cooperate with the political police.

Gosling decided that he could regard Haron's pains and general malaise as 'flu and therefore gave him the appropriate pills. He recognized that Haron's heart-beat was rather fast for 'flu, but it was safer to take this course than to ask the detainee what was causing the pain. He was only too glad that Haron 'was a nervous type . . . a very quiet type' and only smiled. If this was 'flu, he ventured, Haron would have been ill for perhaps two days prior to the consultation; but to inquire why the police had not allowed him treatment in those two days – that would be breaking dangerous ground. Haron overcame his reserve sufficiently to say that he had seen another district surgeon ten days previously, but what self-respecting district surgeon would pay attention to such talkativeness on the part of a detainee? Dr Gosling's findings were of greater interest to the police than to Haron: there was no danger that Haron would collapse and die while enjoying their hospitality!

Inquest:

van Wyk : *From 2 July to 11 July, I saw him every day*
except for the weekend of 5 July. We, the deceased and I,
conversed in my office while I was busy preparing his
statement in writing. The statement was completed on 11
July 1969, and signed the same day. It covered 43 typed
pages . . .

Sworn Affidavit of William Rubin Hare: A. van Wyk told me that
I should not be stubborn as I would be systematically beaten up . . .
He told me never to say I was beaten up and if I did, I would face
the consequences . . . At this stage the magistrate arrived, but I
did not report the assault as I feared further assaults when he was
gone . . . Furthermore that I did not report my assaults to the
magistrate for fear of reprisals by the Security Police and that
this is the case with the detainees . . . I started writing my state-
ment, but Kruger rejected the contents . . . Welman instructed me
to start writing my whole history since I finished school.

Sworn Statement of Belinda Martin: I was taken to a district
surgeon in town . . . I didn't answer any of the doctor's questions.
I had difficulty in walking, and he must have seen the swelling on
my body. He checked me over. He gave me tablets for migraine,
although I didn't complain of one. He asked me if I had been
assaulted. I didn't say I had been – it wouldn't have served any
purpose . . . The next day my nose started bleeding, and I started

96

*retching and my bowels produced blood. I didn't ask to see a
doctor . . . Then the Friday of the next week, I think, a magistrate
came to see me. I couldn't tell him anything. I just couldn't
communicate with him – I saw no purpose being served. He
asked a number of questions. I didn't reply. He must have seen
I wasn't washed, that my clothes were dirty and that the cell was
filthy and smelled.*

The police could get nothing out of the youths of Haron's
congregation whom they had detained, but other avenues were
open to them. Haron's inability to give them names would not
be permitted to prevent them producing witnesses to testify
against him to ensure a long term in jail. They therefore
brought a witness from Port Elizabeth (who, they alleged, had
received money from him) to make a positive identification. To
their chagrin, the witness was unable to identify Haron.
Stymied, they then decided on a more drastic step: Haron was
photographed and copies of the photograph were issued to
detectives who then scoured the city looking for people who
could testify to his 'misdeeds'. Not one was forthcoming. The
people whom Haron had helped had sworn to him that they
would tell no one. No evidence against the Ibadurahman
Study Circle could be unearthed. No cells of the Pan-Africanist
Congress could be found.

From time to time Haron was removed from his cell and
taken to be seen by a possible witness – all to no avail. Thus
when the magistrate was due to see him on 21 July, no visit was
possible. Haron was not available at the time. The magistrate
raised a disconcerted eyebrow but thought: better safe than
sorry. The incident – or lack of it – had to be swept under the
carpet.

The gaps in Haron's story were now becoming a positive
embarrassment. The police belief that they would be able to fill
in the gaps in Haron's story with information known to be
missing on 11 July, had been misplaced. Haron had been
persuasive enough to pacify them for a time, but finally the lack
of names proved too much for Genis and his colleagues to
accept. Genis therefore decided to return to his old persuasive
and friendly ploy: Haron was promised that he would be
released immediately if only he would supply the names of

those working with him. Haron refused. Genis had one last hope: they had observed Haron slyly secreting on his person the ball-point he had been given to write his statement, in the belief that he was not being observed; experience told that prisoners in this position usually tried to smuggle notes out and Haron had ample toilet paper for writing purposes; perhaps he would give something away in such notes? Haron's cell was carefully watched for notes and, in the event, he smuggled out a lengthy letter written on biscuit wrappings the day after Genis suggested that he could be released, 26 July 1969. The police, however, failed to intercept it. This ploy too therefore misfired.

Haron's letter:

> Cell 164,
> Caledon Square
> 26.7.69
> 58th day of detention

Dear Mujaheed,
I am held under the Terrorism Act. They can keep me up till 3 years.

Sorry I left my typewriter behind. I am in good health and high spirits. Don't reply until I inform you. It's a queer place to write to you from but what else can I do. I've got to get in touch with you – praying that you are all in good health. Sacrifices must be made for a good cause.

Everything we discussed at ——'s home in 1966 is an open secret with the S/B. The S/B spoke amongst themselves and I overheard this comment: 'As (Mujaheed) net weet hoe —— sy gat virkoop?' [If (Mujaheed) only knows how —— is selling him out]. It's hard to believe. I just can't get over it. But be careful. Don't tell ——. Make your own investigation.

My meeting with C.C. Your instructions etc. They have it on paper: the full list of code names.

When I returned in 1966 I spoke to —— and —— and told them everything of your instructions. My meeting in Cairo etc. and everything is on paper at the S/B. They told me he is a softie. They hate the guts of ——.

In 1966 dear old —— . . . told me to be careful of —— and —— and I heeded his advice. I refused to give —— money as I've already told you.

98

In 1966 I gave —— an address for you. Mrs —— and I told —— to get in touch with you. According to the S/B this letter was written to you but —— did not write it. He had someone to write it and that person brought the letter to them S/B. You've got all in a nutshell.

The S/B want information out of me:

(1) who are those working with me – I took everything on my own. I told them I am alone . . .

(2) They uplifted the R4000 which I received in 1966–1967–1968 through my banks.

They want to know who are the recipients of funds. I told them that I gave the money to schools, churches and mosques and I used some for myself. They are still looking for those poor people. But those people took an oath by me that they won't spill. And I must thank Allah that they stand by their word.

The S/B issued their detectives with my photo to go into the location. But I depend on Allah alone. He is great. He is my saviour.

They feel that I operated Defence and Aid [which] is banned and am feeding banned people, creating Poqo cells: I will give my life but never will I divulge any of my companions.

[Mujaheed] please be careful what you do. These people [S/B] are planning to assassinate or kidnap you. I don't know whether they are bluffing or what. They say that their overseas intelligence is powerful, also they are training Africans to leave RSA and join ANC and PAC and they [are informing]. They told me yesterday I must supply the names of those working with me, then I can go home! I am negative. No sir . . .

There was a leak in the P.E. depot. But their informer failed to identify me, so it fell through. The other depot was feeding before I was taken as I took an overdraft at my bank. Only my C.F. and R.I. children are starving for the time being.

[Mujaheed] whatever we discussed alone is still a tight secret. Only Allah knows. I will send you another cover address as soon as I am released. Also don't worry. There is no vacuum . . . Give Canon my prayers and Abraham also . . . I've got no more space left.

Imam

Haron, meanwhile believed that the police had insufficient

evidence on which to charge him in a court of law – whatever their suspicions might be. He continued to entertain the idea that they would finally have to release him. In that event, he decided he would leave the country. Even then it worried him that another country might not accept him. But he put such thoughts aside, to be sorted out another day. At this stage he remained confident, in good health and was generally in fine spirits. He had recovered from the beating.

Inquest:

(1) COOPER : *Did you get a statement from the deceased?*
    GENIS : *Yes.*
    COOPER : *Was it a complete statement?*
    GENIS : *Well, I found the statement riddled with lies.*

(2) VAN WYK : *. . . at the first stage he made a statement that was completely false. After a time he started talking the truth . . . we decided on 2 July to make the written statement . . . Well, we believed it was true and that is why we put the statement in writing . . . later we discovered that much of it was also false.*

All attempts to get further information from Abdulla Haron failed. With the passage of time the need to have him close at hand, right in Caledon Square, to check and cross-check with questions and possible witnesses became less urgent. No witnesses could be pulled out of the available hats to attempt to identify him. Consequently, Haron was removed on 11 August to a police station in the suburb of Maitland three or four miles from the city.

The cell at Maitland was a comparatively large one, measuring 13 feet 10 inches by 8 feet. It had two large windows. In one corner was a lavatory. Once more there was no bed, and not even a bunk or bench. The door was secured by the normal lock and by another padlock, one key being kept in the safe in the charge-office, while the other was kept by the driver of the patrol van. No one individual could gain access to Haron on their own. There were two small exercise yards and one large one measuring about 50 feet by 20 feet. Sometimes Haron was restricted to a small yard and at others he was allowed the use of the larger yard. He could exercise for half an hour at a time, sometimes in the morning and sometimes in the afternoon.

Was it worth it, Haron wondered, going on holding out like this? Was the struggle worth it? So many people had left the country since 1960, patriots and politicians. He had lost so many good friends. Was there anything he regretted? Yes, there were things he would have done differently now, with the benefit of hindsight, but on the whole he was reasonably satisfied. He had chosen the right path and had stuck to it.

God knows the black people had made enough compromises in the past, but now their time had come. Now they must learn to have pride in themselves, to love freedom enough even to die for it. They must learn too to hate their oppressors and to have the courage to fight and destroy the tyranny to which they were subjected. He had prayed that things might turn out differently. But what could a man do when praying seemed to be not enough?

They accused him of pride – false pride – which stopped him from squealing. Maybe they were right. Perhaps it was pride; but was it so wrong to have pride? Pride in his own achievements and those of others who had been this way before? They wanted to destroy his pride, to make him betray his friends, his people, his cause. A man must be loyal to the things he loves. Loyalty is an expression of love. Haron loved Allah, he loved Islam, he loved his friends, and he loved freedom. To these he would remain loyal.

Ah, to be free, Haron mused, free to face another man squarely and speak freely, to be able openly to agree or to disagree. The freedom he was being offered was a shadow of that real freedom, a freedom bought with the lives of others. Could he, a man of God, turn betrayer? Never! The right to change his mind, yes. But betrayal . . .

What of his family? They were suffering now – perhaps more than he was. But what was even that to the suffering which grips the whole world in its talons? They would understand. The struggle for freedom was everybody's struggle.

The drama had now reached the point when Haron could be detained indefinitely under these conditions. His captors were determined to impress upon him that his position was utterly hopeless; Genis and his colleagues would pay him an occasional visit to make sure he remained aware of his complete subjuga-

101

tion to, and dependence on, them. Sometimes they would ask him whether he was ready to talk.

On 21 August, Haron was removed for the day from Maitland police station. Once again, this incident was timed to take place just after the Monday visit of the magistrate. Having been unable either to obtain witnesses or extract the relevant information from Haron, the police were becoming frustrated. Meanwhile they had confirmed that the London Muslim Welfare Association did not and had never existed and that money had not been transferred to Haron's account by any organization of that name.

Once more therefore Spyker and Andries were given their way with Haron. Once more he was forced to undress. Now they put a sack over his head. Somebody held him down and he felt them fiddling with his fingers. They were attaching something, and then they spoke about 'the voltage'. 'Twenty-five volts'. A machine hummed and Haron felt his body shudder as the electric charge surged through him. His whole body seemed to be burning. 'Fifty volts.' And he was shrieking as his frame seemed to twist and buck. 'Two hundred volts.' And Haron's prayers became a continuous howl as his joints seemed to turn to water: his body felt as though it wished to fly apart. 'Talk! Talk! Names! Names!' the bellows came faintly through to Haron. The only speech he could produce, the only name he could say, was a continuous call: 'Bilal! Bilal! Bi-lal . . . !' The operation was repeated with the electrodes attached to his genitals. He lost consciousness.

They got no further information from Haron except for confirmation of some they already had on their files. It was at 10 o'clock that night, under cover of darkness, that the crumpled body of Haron was returned to his cell in Maitland by the 'sympathetic' Major Genis.

The Authors have been informed by Abdul Jassat (90-day detainee, 1963, who organized the escape of himself, Moola, Wolpe and Goldreich out of detention) that the electric torture to which he was subjected followed a similar procedure.

In order to break Haron's routine and to add to his sense of insecurity and tension, the fortnightly visit of the magistrate due on September 1 did not take place. Instead, the magistrate called on Wednesday, 3 September. On Sunday,14 September, Haron discovered blood in his excrement. He had suffered from piles for a long time, and the condition had been aggravated by his state of tension. He requested medical attention and was seen in his cell by Dr Gosling on this Sunday and the next day, Monday. Indeed, the order that Haron should be given the necessary attention on this occasion came from no less a personage than the chief of Cape Town's Security Branch, Colonel Pienaar. Dr Gosling had been found quite 'cooperative' by the political police on the previous occasion and they saw no need to send for Dr Viviers. In any case, the more obvious marks of the torture inflicted $3\frac{1}{2}$ weeks previously had now disappeared, and Haron was to be seen in his cell rather than in the doctor's surgery.

Suppositories were prescribed but Dr Gosling was pleased to confirm that in other respects Abdulla Haron appeared to be in good health. The implication that he could, as in the case of John Schlapoberskey, be 'ridden' was not lost on his jailers. But to 'ride' Haron, special arrangements had to be made. They had at an earlier interrogation suggested to Haron that he would not leave the prison alive if he did not give the names of his accomplices. Haron's reaction had confirmed their worst fears: he would take his chances on that – although he thought they were bluffing. Not so, they replied – as he would discover. They would first get the information and then they would not bother how he ended up.

To ensure this convenient sequence of events it was necessary to obtain the services of the most highly-skilled torturers, for the run-of-the-mill variety might kill their victim prematurely. First, a medical report to the effect that he would not suddenly die while being 'ridden' was essential. Special arrangements also had to be made with Pretoria.

At 7.42 a.m. on the morning of Wednesday, 17 September – two days after the last medical examination by Dr Gosling and a fortnight precisely after the previous visit of the magistrate – Abdulla Haron was once more removed from the cells of Maitland police station by Major Dirk Genis. Once more he was taken to Caledon Square.

HARON : Look, Major Genis, why don't you charge me or

103

release me? I have nothing further to tell you.

GENIS : You live in hopes, don't you? I can tell you this: we will keep you for ever if necessary, in order to get further information. There's going to be no easy way out for you.

SPYKER : You are going to spill your guts! We'll see to that!

HARON : I'm telling you no more.

GENIS : So you say now! But you'll be singing a different tune when we're through with you.

HARON : I want to be charged if you've got a case against me. I'm on my own and I accept full responsibility for everything.

SPYKER : You're a fucking liar! You've been exposed! You're a bloody terrorist!

HARON : Then why don't you charge me?

GENIS : There is no question of charging you until we have the names.

SPYKER : Names, you bloody Malay bastard! Names!

HARON : I don't know any names. I was on my own.

GENIS : You can walk out of here a free man if you give the names. But otherwise you'll just stay locked up.

SPYKER : They'll carry you out in a coffin if you don't talk! We are finished playing with you, you black pig!

HARON : Look, I've had enough of this. I'll plead guilty to everything and you can charge me.

SPYKER : Not fucking likely! You are guilty as hell, we know that. But it's names we want. And you are going to give them. We'll take you to Pretoria if necessary! Do you know what that means?

HARON : I've got a right to be tried if I'm guilty of anything.

GENIS : You've got no rights! Don't fool yourself! You are completely in our power. There's nothing, absolutely nothing, that anyone can do to help you now. So you better talk. We've broken better men than you, Imam Haron!

HARON : I've nothing to say.

SPYKER : You are taking your fate in your own hands. You know that, don't you?

HARON : I don't know what you mean.

SPYKER : What's going to happen to you will be completely
your own responsibility! You'll have no one else to blame
but yourself. Don't blame us! We've done our best to be
reasonable!

GENIS : I warn you: you are going to talk! It's better for
you to talk now rather than in Pretoria! They're sick and
tired of you, even on the highest level! So it's Pretoria if
you don't talk now!

SPYKER : These people in Pretoria know their stuff, man!
I've seen them work and they can break any man! You
won't even have a chance to commit suicide, man!

HARON : That's what you call white, Christian civilization?

SPYKER : You deserve nothing better, you swine! And
don't come and insult my religion, you filthy Malay pig!
I'll beat your brains out right now if you insult my
religion.

GENIS : We know how anti-white you are and all the things
you've been saying. But that we'll let go. It's the names we
want! Now talk, dammit!

HARON : I've got nothing to say.

GENIS : Well, OK. The Colonel has decided to have a word
with you to try to make you see reason before your fate is
sealed. Come with me.

Haron was ushered into the elegant office of Lieutenant
Colonel Carel Johannes Freysen Pienaar. Genis was asked to
leave and he was alone with the Colonel. Beautiful bookcases
surrounded the Colonel who was seated at his magnificent desk.
Large photographs of the bigwigs of the Boer State gazed at the
detainee from the walls. The Colonel was very friendly and
welcomed Haron with a smile and a warm handshake. He
invited Haron to sit down.

PIENAAR : How are you, Imam Haron?

HARON : As well as can be expected.

PIENAAR : Yes, well, I'm sorry that we should meet only in
these circumstances. Can I offer you some tea?

HARON : No, thank you. I avoid these things during the
day.

PIENAAR : Oh, yes, I was forgetting. Is everything all right
with your food? Your religious practices are being
respected?

HARON : Yes, everything is all right, Colonel.

PIENAAR : Good, I'm glad . . . now, as to the purpose of our little talk . . . As you can see we are entirely alone and I have given instructions that we are not to be disturbed. So you need not be afraid and hold back. Everything said here will be just between us. Man to man, you know. Is that all right with you?

HARON : That's all right, Colonel.

PIENAAR : I can tell you that your family is all right. They miss you, of course . . . but then, that is to be expected, isn't it? I'm sure you feel the same way yourself, hey, Imam?

HARON : Yes, I miss my family.

PIENAAR : I understand that you have a daughter overseas? You must be very ambitious for her. Is she a clever girl?

HARON : Just normal. But she is hardworking and wants to get on.

PIENAAR : Yes, it's good if the children take an interest in their education. And the younger ones? Are they also like that?

HARON : Yes.

PIENAAR : You must be very proud of your children. You are a good family man, from what I hear. I also believe in a good family life. The family is the basis of society, not so, Imam?

HARON : Yes, I think one's family is important.

PIENAAR : I can assure you, I don't like keeping a good family man away from his family like this. As far as I am concerned, I would like you to be able to go home straight away. But I've got my job to do, you see. You do understand, don't you, Imam?

HARON : Yes, I understand, Colonel.

PIENAAR : Wouldn't you like to be able to go home straight away?

HARON : Who wouldn't? Solitary confinement is hell! I wouldn't treat a dog like this.

PIENAAR : As I say, I am only doing my job. I don't like it – not a bit. But the law is the law, you know. The decision isn't in my hands, you see. I can make a recommendation. And my recommendation carries a lot of weight in

Pretoria. If you just give us a little more cooperation, I am certain Pretoria will agree to your release. You could be back with your family in a very short time. What do you think of that?

HARON : It sounds nice, Colonel. But I've given all the cooperation I can.

PIENAAR : Aren't you worried about your family then?

HARON : Of course I am. And I don't know why you people don't take me to court or release me. Of course I want to go home. But if it's a question of going to jail, I just have to accept that.

PIENAAR : But there is no need for that . . . We don't want to send you to jail. If you cooperate you can walk out of here a free man with no more trouble from us. I give you my word!

HARON : Colonel Pienaar, you people say you've caught me out. Then charge me, because I can't stand this solitary confinement and continuous interrogation and tension any more. I want to go home or to jail and get it over with!

PIENAAR : Are you perhaps worried that the people overseas will get at your daughter if you cooperate with us?

HARON : Yes.

PIENAAR : But we can arrange for her to come home without much trouble. And here she will have the best protection in the world! You see, there's no need to worry.

HARON : Look, Colonel, lay a charge in open court and get the matter over with. There is nothing more I can tell you people.

PIENAAR : If you went to jail it would be for a very long time, you know. You might even get a death sentence, but here I'm offering you a way out with no come-backs. It's a genuine offer, man!

HARON : I'm prepared to die for my principles if it comes to that, Colonel, but you haven't got such a case against me. How long could they put me away for?

PIENAAR : A very long time. I couldn't say exactly how long, but it could be a very long time. After all, look at all the things you've been involved in. You visited London in 1966 and received instructions from persons who we know to be terrorists to recruit people in the Republic of South Africa, send them out and have them trained as terrorists.

107

For this purpose you had to create an organization in your mosque which would be known as the Ibadurahman Study Circle. The purpose was to enlist young men under the pretext of sending them on the Muslim pilgrimage. During this period they would visit China where they would undergo terrorist training and thereafter return home. For this purpose you received large sums of money, and it would be your duty to pay the fares of the terrorists. We believe that you *did* gather recruits and that you *did* send them overseas. You travelled around the country gathering recruits. You also had to go to Maseru to hand over the money received from London to the leaders there of the Pan-Africanist Congress. You also had instructions to go to Botswana where you were to meet terrorist leaders and with them work out routes along which terrorists could be taken in and out of the country.

Now, Imam, this record of terrorist activity is enough to make anyone's hair stand on end! It just can't be allowed! There is no country in the world which would allow it. But we are understanding people. I know, all kinds of people, you included, sometimes say bad things about the South African police. But we are not as bad as some people make us out. You see, we know you have been misled. Perhaps you have some kind of grievance which helped these Communists and terrorists to ensnare you in their web of intrigue. Well, that's something which can always be settled another way. However, we are still prepared to let bygones be bygones if you'll cooperate. All we want is the names of the people involved.

HARON : I only knew people by code-names.

PIENAAR : I don't know how you can say that. It's impossible! Look, let me put it to you this way: these people overseas talk very big and boast about all the things they have done and are going to do; but they leave people like you – ordinary, decent people – to do the dirty work. You must see that they have just misled you . . . And I can tell you this, if you decided to cooperate with us you would not be the first person to do so, you know. Some of those big talkers are actually working for us! Right at the moment, we are even training Africans to go overseas, pretending that they want to be trained as guerillas. But they will actually be working for us! These terrorists can *never* win, Imam Haron, *never*! The South African State is too powerful for them. So you see, you'll be backing a loser if you persist with this business.

HARON : No, sir. I can't help you. I don't know any names.

PIENAAR : Look, we're all alone here. Nothing you say to me need go beyond these walls. We can work something out. I think I've heard you were interested in leaving the country. Even that can be arranged. It's been done before, you know. Right out of solitary confinement into an aeroplane. Only the other day we did that for a Jew named Schlapobersky. And there have been others too . . .

And on . . . and on. But Haron remained adamant: he had nothing further to say, knew no names. Finally Pienaar pressed a button to summon Genis. He turned to Haron and said, 'I'm sorry that you insist on being so stubborn. But it's your own fate you've sealed. I won't bear any hard feelings against you and I hope you feel the same way.' And having thus exculpated himself, he informed Genis, 'He is all yours!'

Inquest (1):

COOPER : *Captain Malan, the deceased, you say, was brought to Maitland police station on 11 August?*

MALAN : *That is correct.*

COOPER : *But how many times was the deceased taken from the police cells?*

MALAN : *The accused was taken out on two occasions . . . The first time was at 7.50 a.m. on 21st of the eighth month and he was brought back at about 10.00 p,m, on the same day. The second occasion that he was taken out was on the 17th of the ninth month at 7.42 a.m. . . . He was brought back at 9.40 p.m. on the 19th of the ninth month.*

Inquest (2):

PIENAAR : *The 17/9/69 was the last time I saw the deceased alive in the State security police office in Cape Town. For about two and a half hours I interviewed the deceased. The deceased sat on a chair during the interview . . . (it was) in the morning. I was alone with him.*

109

Genis was in a hurry. The palaver about visits by a magistrate was inconvenient but served as an excellent cover to hide a multitude of sins. Therefore the magistrate had to be sent for to come and take his normal perfunctory glance at Haron. This was arranged, and then he handed Haron over to the ever-faithful Spyker van Wyk. Major Genis decided that there was no more he could do – the matter was now out of his hands. He would go and have a restful evening at home while Spyker got on with the job in hand.

Spyker had for company on this occasion two sinister-looking strangers Haron had not seen before. They were not members of the South African police but had been specially brought in to 'break' Haron, and finalize the case. It was now late afternoon and with their fast car they were satisfied that they could reach their mystery destination at a reasonable hour. Arrangements had been made for a room and a team of men to be placed at their disposal. Off they went, taking care to avoid any prying eyes. They drove quickly through the city traffic, watching Haron carefully for any attempt to escape or draw attention to himself; and they soon slipped on to the broad dual carriageway at the start of the magnificent National Road.

When they arrived, Abdulla Haron knew that he was entitled to fear the worst as he was marched through gate after gate within a large building. He found himself in a large bare room where he was shortly joined by a number of very large men. They looked amused at the sight of the little Imam. Haron felt his heart beating like a drum and he dreaded that the giants surrounding him would hear it. His stomach churned and he felt like vomiting; but his stomach was empty, it was many hours since he had eaten. Fearfully he watched every movement of the pack around him and under his breath began chanting to himself: 'La ilaaha Illal-lah!'

'Soften him up a bit,' ordered one of Spyker's companions. The three then walked out, leaving Haron to the mercy of the big men.

Haron was given a few smacks . . . then a few kicks . . . he was punched . . . and then a man much taller than him began drumming with big fists on his head. Roars of laughter and cursing rang about his ears. He screamed with pain. 'Ahad! Ahad!' he moaned breathlessly as the blows fell on his head.

110

His tormentors decided to make 'the circumcised pig' undress and then abuse him in this condition. Haron was forced to undress and was then flung on the floor. One of the torturers grabbed his genitals and gave a twist. 'Allah! Allah!' howled the little Imam. Amidst the bellows of 'Talk you filth', one brought forth a baton and gently patted his penis with it, threatening to beat it to pulp. Through his pain, Haron prayed under his breath that he might escape from his surroundings, and then tried to will himself into unconsciousness. But the attentions of his tormentors forced him back into the terrifying present.

Four hefty men held him down and the one with the baton stood over him, threatening once more. 'Are you going to talk or do you want your balls smashed?' he screamed.

'La-ilaaha Illal-lah!' groaned Haron.

The 'baton-man' smashed the baton down on Haron's thigh, just missing his genitals. They responded to Haron's shrieks of pain by condemning 'baton-man's' bad aim. 'Smash his fucking balls to bits and make sure he can't bring any more like himself into the world!' they roared. 'Kill the black filth!' they roared. 'End his fucking days for ever!' roared one of the wits. 'The thing won't stand up! Beat some life into it!' they roared. 'I'm not going to miss this time!' roared 'baton-man', 'are you going to talk?'

'Ahad! Ahad!' shouted Haron.

'Baton-man' patted Haron's penis gently once more. 'You are going to talk, pig!' He swung and brought the baton down viciously almost on the same place on Haron's groin. They continued for a while longer, banging on Haron's head and giving him a karate chop here and there. Then they left him in a groaning heap.

Later Spyker and the mystery-men reappeared. They wanted to know whether Haron was prepared to talk. He had nothing to add to what he had already said. So they then brought in a beam of wood and rested this on high stilts. Haron was instructed to place his right leg over the beam, with his knee almost touching his chin. His left leg almost buckled under the strain. The mystery-men then came up behind him and deftly inserted a needle into the lower part of his spinal column.

Haron's shrieks and howls of pain left them unmoved. Tears streamed down his face and he bellowed to Allah to deliver him from this hell; to strike him dead on the spot; to take him up into the heavens. He fainted and fell heavily to the floor. The mystery-men calmly removed their needle and called for water to douse him and bring him back to consciousness.

Once more Haron was strung over the beam. Once more they inserted their needle, but not so deep this time. They touched the needle gently so that it would scrape against bone. Every touch reduced Haron to paroxysms of agony. The mystery-men were quite unmoved.

Spyker looked on admiringly. He felt very privileged to watch such experts at work. The mystery-men warned Haron even as he wept and howled that his every movement would cause the needle to scrape the bone. They advised him to talk soon if he wished to be relieved.

The strain on Haron's left leg was almost unbearable and yet he had to try not to move at all because of the terrible needle. The mystery-men proceeded to fire their questions at him. Haron gave them truthful answers. When an answer seemed not completely satisfactory they touched the needle. They worked quickly. The whole investigation of the past four months was rapidly covered although Haron occasionally fell down and fainted.

They came to the question of the names of his associates. Haron screamed: 'You can kill me but I will never divulge any names.' The mystery-men kicked Haron's left leg from under him. Once more he was doused with ice-cold water and placed over the beam. They repeated their question. 'Ahah! Ahad! Bilal! Bilal!' shrieked Haron. They vibrated the needle vigorously, and once more Haron fainted and fell. This happened a few times.

The mystery-men turned to Spyker: 'We will kill him if we continue. It's no use, we will have to leave it there for the present.'

Spyker looked upset. 'But we have to get him back to Cape Town. We can't delay here,' he said.

'You don't want a corpse on your hands do you?' they asked. 'No, no! Definitely not. He is more valuable to us alive than dead,' he replied, quite aghast at the consequences of such a mishap.

'Exactly! So the thing to do is to take him back and keep him in cold storage a little longer. We can have another go at a later stage,' they said.

'For my part, I would like to smash his stinking brains in all over the walls. But that's out of the question at the moment,' snarled the disappointed Spyker.

'Well, if you were as experienced as we are, you would realize that some of these creatures do die before they tell you anything,' they said philosophically. 'You're lucky that you got so much out of him. That was due to good previous intelligence. Take it from us, if you had not had that previous intelligence, you'd have got nothing!'

The needle was then removed and Haron was lifted off the beam. He was left to lie in a heap while the three torturers went to eat and rest before starting the journey back to Cape Town. Before setting off that evening, Haron was allowed to dress and was then bundled back into the car.

It was Friday afternoon when Spyker and his mystery-men delivered Haron back to Caledon Square. Deeply aggrieved, Spyker reported to his colleagues that he had some additional facts but still no names. Curses of disappointment swept the corridors of Security Branch headquarters, and some wanted a last go at Haron but Spyker regretfully decided that matters should be allowed to remain as they were for the moment.

That evening, Genis and Spyker returned Haron to his cell in the police station at Maitland once more. It was a very convenient time for another reason: being Friday evening, the tortured, staggering Haron could very easily be taken for an arrested drunk being locked up for the night. They had organized the whole thing marvellously. But it was, from their point of view, a pity about the names.

Inquest (1):

COOPER : *We have now discovered from Captain Malan that the deceased was not kept at Maitland police station for the period, 17 September, 7.42 a.m. to the night of 19 September 1969 – a very crucial period of time in this whole matter, and this is the first time this has been elicited . . . I think everybody has been under the impression that after his interrogation he was taken back to Maitland, but we now have it that over a period of time he wasn't in fact at the place where he was normally detained.*

113

Inquest (2):

PROSECUTOR : *He was taken out on investigation and he was not even in the Cape Peninsula at the time. They took him out to various places as far as I can make out . . . I think in the interest of the State I feel that we should not disclose where – although he was not here in the Cape Peninsula – we are not prepared to disclose where they had taken him to . . .*

Inquest (3):

VAN WYK : *He wasn't questioned for periods, we talked while the car was in motion.*

COOPER : *Who were present?*

VAN WYK : *I am not prepared to say who were with us . . . not only members of the police were present.*

COOPER : *Who then were the other persons?*

VAN WYK : *Other persons who were not members of the police force . . . No unauthorized person came into contact with the deceased.*

COOPER : *Who were they?*

VAN WYK : *No, I am not prepared to say.*

COOPER : *I only want to know who the police officer was?*

VAN WYK : *I was the only police officer.*

COOPER : *Where was Major Genis?*

VAN WYK : *He was not present.*

COOPER : *When did Major Genis join you on the 19th?*

VAN WYK : *It was at about . . . during the afternoon of the 19th. After two.*

House of Parliament, 18.9.1970: Mrs Catherine Taylor, MP: I want to tell the house that my information, from confidential sources, is that Sergeant Andries van Wyk was involved in the assault upon the prisoner and that this assault was directly responsible for the subsequent decline in his physical condition during the last week of his life, which finally led to the Imam's death on 27 September.

Sworn Statement: Belinda Martin: Also I was not given any food or water for the next two weeks, and only survived by drinking water from the toilet pan in my cell from the fourth day after my arrest.

*　　　　　*　　　　　*

Sworn Affidavit: William Rubin Hare: My head was clean-shaven and Visser also joined the assault by repeatedly hitting me on the head. This continued for approximately an hour.

The Authors have been personally informed by Hennie Ferus (90-day detainee, 1963) that a certain Sergeant Louw attempted to insert a needle into his spine.

Chapter Nine

The Passion of Abdulla Haron

Driven and hunted by men,
They make us helpless and condemn;
Bearing the burden of our abusers,
It is we who are the accusers.

(*Pastor Dietrich Bonhoeffer, Anti-Nazi
Professor of Theology hanged by the Nazis
on 9 April 1945. Poem smuggled from
a cell in Tegel [Germany].*)

Abdulla Haron could hardly crawl under his blankets. His
world was a blaze of pain and torment. He could not kneel to
say his midnight prayers and could not turn to face in the
direction of Mecca. But if these things are not possible they are
forgiven. He lay in the most comfortable position he could
manage and very quietly mumbled his prayers. He begged for-
giveness of his sins and humbly requested Allah to relieve him
of his painful life. This was a trial such as Bilal himself had
suffered. Fleeting doubts had brushed his mind, but now there
was no room for doubt: all things shall be restored to the faithful in the end. He must trust Allah and rely on the just vengeance
which would be visited upon his torturers.

Wracked with pain, both mental and physical, Haron was
also overcome with exhaustion. He had hardly slept for three

days, only managing to catch a few winks while sitting in the police car. His body lacked the strength to remain awake because he had had no food in three days either. Consequently he passed into a fitful doze, awakened from time to time by a stab of pain and now and again by a dream-like fear which flashed a warning of danger across his quiescent brain.

The following morning, Saturday 20 September, Haron was feeling just a little better after the night's rest. He managed to stagger to his feet despite the enveloping pain which ripped through his body with every movement. Dominating all else was the thunder of a violent headache, the like of which he had never experienced. And yet he could not bear to raise his arms and use his hands to hold his bursting skull together. He felt himself surrounded by enemies and wished only to be left in peace to suffer alone, as a dying animal removes itself to some hidden corner away from its fellows. But with such a headache as this, produced by the drubbing of the fists of his tormentors, there could be no peace. 'A doctor, a doctor, please get me a doctor!' Haron moaned at the constable who first came to his cell. Seeing his shocking state, the constable immediately hastened to call Captain Malan, the officer in charge of Maitland police station.

'What is the matter,' gasped Malan, aghast at the appalling state of Haron.

'My head, my head, I can't stand it! I need a doctor,' begged Haron.

'You wait. I will phone Security Branch straight away,' gasped Malan, and hastened to the telephone.

Malan spoke to Captain Geldenhuys who was the officer on duty at Security Branch. It being Saturday, Genis was not on duty and Geldenhuys's efforts to contact him were unavailing. Nevertheless his orders were clear: no doctor should be allowed to see Haron. Notwithstanding these instructions, the concern and upset apparent at Maitland police station had to be allayed, and Geldenhuys therefore hastened there on his own. He would see what he could do to smooth things over. He went to see Haron.

'Please, I have a violent headache,' begged Haron, 'get me a doctor.'

'I can't do that,' replied Geldenhuys. 'My orders are that you must not be allowed to see a doctor unless you provide the further information we need!'

'Oh, God,' moaned Haron, 'can't you just give me something for the headache?'

'I'll ask about that. You'll have to wait until I can get something,' replied Geldenhuys. But he felt anxious about the man's condition, and the staff of the police station were looking at him and at one another very meaningfully. 'Is there anything I can do for you?' he asked Haron.

'My whole inside is burning. Can I have something cold?' begged Haron.

His orders did not cover this, so Geldenhuys felt it would be in order for Haron to have something. He sent a probationary constable for an ice-cream and a cold mineral drink, and let Haron have these.

'Why don't you get a doctor instead of all these things,' asked the uniformed police inquisitively.

'The district surgeon is not available today,' lied Geldenhuys. He nevertheless sought permission to provide Haron with some pain-killing pills because none were available at the police station. That afternoon Geldenhuys dashed out to his good friend Dr Viviers in Bellville to get some of the same pills which had been prescribed by him on the previous occasion. He left four of these for Haron's use at the police station, claiming that he had got them from his own home, thereby making a great show of his own humanity. Geldenhuys then took Captain Malan aside and informed him that Haron was not to be allowed to see a doctor and that, furthermore, Malan should use the pain-killing pills sparingly, to avoid giving Haron any relief from pain as far as was possible. He also passed on an instruction from higher authority that Haron's clean clothing should not be accepted from his family when they brought it later in the week. The intention, he informed Malan, was to debase Haron so far that he would become completely dependent on Major Genis, and eventually give the information required. Geldenhuys wondered whether anything could be done about preventing Haron from getting the food his family brought? Captain Malan would see what could be done.

That evening Haron ate some of the fruit and biscuits he had in his cell. He managed to kneel in the direction of Mecca and spent the evening praying. He tried to remain immobile so that his broken rib would not be disturbed, so that the hell which gnawed at the base of his spine would not flare up in anger, so that the bones and sinews and muscles and nerves of his shoulders, his hips, his thighs, his shins, his ankles might rest and recuperate in peace, and so that his thundering head might thunder less mightily. In the end he slept as well as a human body so savagely mawled was capable.

The following morning, Sunday, Haron found that his headache was less severe. That pain had heretofore blotted out many of his other ills, and its abatement served now merely to draw attention to the raging agony of the broken rib. Every rise and fall of his chest provoked a war of contending nerve-ends, each seemingly bent on destroying the others in a mad clamour for supremacy. As soon as he could he attracted Captain Malan's attention. But, in vain. Malan deflected his appeals by saying that he would phone the Security Branch, whose responsibility Haron really was, to ask them to call on him. Meanwhile he bravely dissuaded Haron from taking the pain-killing pills because too many were no good for him. He felt enormously pleased with himself at having rendered this assistance to the great Major Genis. He then phoned Genis who was overjoyed to hear of Haron's agony and quickly sent one of his minions to sneer at and deride the unfortunate prisoner: names first, medical attention after!

Ah, it's going so well now, thought Genis at the steering wheel of his car the next morning while on his way to work: everybody was being so cooperative – except Haron, of course. Another week, perhaps two, and the little bastard would be broken. He could quite safely, he felt, pop in on Haron – although it was only 7.30 a.m. – and put on a great show of friendship. The little Imam would by now be feeling a growing need for human sympathy and understanding; and he, Genis, would be there bright and early to provide both.

'Hello, Imam Haron. How are you feeling today, man,' oozed Genis, 'I hear you've been sick, hey? Sorry I was away for a few days and I couldn't come to see you personally, man. Hope you're feeling better, hey?'

'My headache is back. I've got a headache again,' moaned Haron, trying to get up.

'Don't get up. Don't get up. It's quite OK,' sympathized Genis as he went down on one knee beside Haron's blankets. 'Headache, hey? Why don't you ask them for some pills, hey? Abdulla, man – you don' mind if I call you Abdulla, hey? We've known one another so long, hey?'

'I wish I could get some pills, Major,' murmured Haron.

'I'll fix it up, straight away, then,' Genis reassured him and trotted off eagerly to the charge-office to fetch the pills. He got some water in Haron's mug and assisted him to take the pills.

'Feeling better now?' asked Genis in his most solicitous manner.

'Yes. Actually I need a doctor, Major,' murmured Haron painfully. 'I think my rib's broken.'

'A doctor? Broken rib?' Genis feigned great concern and looked grave. 'How did that happen? When?'

'The other day. They beat me up,' whispered Haron.

'Beat you up?' Genis feigned horror. 'Now I don' uphold with that kin' of thing. You leave it with me. I will go into this an' put a stop to it.'

Haron could hardly believe his ears. 'And, Major, I'm very hungry. I haven't received my food for a few days,' he moaned plaintively.

'Sorry to hear that, Abdulla,' murmured Genis. 'Don' worry. I'll get it fixed up. I'll go an' see right away.'

Before Haron could recover from the confusion produced by this favourable turn of events, Genis had said goodbye and slipped out.

Haron now found that his stomach was beginning to take revenge upon him for failing to cater, albeit through no fault of his own, to its just demands. He had already consumed the odd few bits of stale biscuit and fruit that he had had in his cell, but this had been as nothing against the number of days he had been without his evening meal. To the pains of the rest of his body were now added the pangs of his stomach, coupled with a general weakness due to starvation. The cumulative effect took the form of an overpowering dread of the future. The confidence and optimism which had sustained him for so long now almost evaporated. His every waking moment became filled with anxiety. But a thought stirred: there was one hope. Perhaps Genis was really a decent chap. Genis had not participated in

121

any of the assaults and tortures; he had sounded so friendly today and offered to protect him; he had said he would put an end to the assaults.

When his food arrived that evening and he could, despite his sorry condition, peck at it, Haron began to feel a certain liking for Genis. Then when the next evening his food once more did not arrive, Haron concluded that it was because Genis had not been there to see that things were in order.

On Wednesday morning Genis once more called at 7.30 a.m., en route to his office. Once more he knelt beside Haron and spoke in a friendly way and called him Abdulla. Haron took his chance and begged for a doctor. Genis was most contrite but claimed that the matter was out of his hand. He would do any-thing he could to help, but somebody somewhere at the top had given orders that Haron must be punished in this way. He hated the order but he could not go against it. Was there anything else he could do? Yes, responded Haron, food! Must have been a slip-up, suggested Genis. He would go and see straight away. And, to be sure, in a few minutes Genis was back with a packet of biscuits and some fruit. He was very sorry, Abdulla. Every-thing has been fixed up now, Abdulla. Haron was most appre-ciative.

Don't rush your fences, Genis told himself; play it cool, take your time; Friday will be a good opportunity to 'pop the question'. He promised Haron in the most friendly manner he could simulate that he would see him on Friday.

Haron's food arrived, as expected, that evening. But it suddenly dawned on him that he should have had clean clothing as well; and clothing suddenly became a matter of the utmost importance. His clean clothing did not arrive the next evening either. Nor did his food. Haron's emotional state became dangerous. He ached and raged and despaired and rallied. 'Genis, Genis! For God's sake, Genis! I want my food! I want my clean clothing! I can't stand this any more!' Haron wept and howled.

The strain on his heart was becoming unbearable and it was with desperation that Haron threw himself down on his prayer-mat and hour after hour grovelled his prayers.

Genis and Spyker conferred lengthily to plan their next move. It was agreed that Haron would now be looking forward to

Genis's arrival early on Friday morning. But they would disappoint him. Genis would not come. Instead they would go together in the afternoon. Genis would approach Haron alone first and after a display of great friendship would invite Haron to confide in him. He would 'pop' the all-important question of 'the names' in the most insinuating manner. If Haron did not cooperate Genis would not become annoyed. He would retain his friendly relationship with Haron and would make a friendly exit. But then Spyker would enter and give Haron a beating while Genis kept watch outside to make sure that nobody intervened. If Haron screamed it would not matter. It was Friday, and on that day nobody paid attention to the screams that came from police stations: it was only the drunkards getting what they deserved! To put Haron in a good frame of mind for Genis's belated arrival they would ensure that the Maitland police gave him some pain-killing pills in the morning. Malan must make sure that Haron was informed that it was on the direct orders of Caledon Square that he was being so well treated.

According to plan, Haron felt disconcerted by the non-arrival of Genis. According to plan, he was plied with pills by his now solicitous captors. That afternoon Genis arrived at Maitland with Spyker. The rest of the plan was then put into operation and, unfortunately, Haron was still unable to provide them with the names they wanted. He was most upset that he could not be of more help, but Genis was effusive in his apologies for broaching such a delicate matter. And, of course, he would have this question of food and clean clothing properly taken care of. He would see Haron on Monday again to make sure he was all right. Abdulla would like to see him on Monday again, wouldn't he? Yes, yes, of course Abdulla would like to see him. Genis then retired and kept watch at the gateway to the exercise yard outside Haron's cell.

'How dare you treat Major Genis like this!' roared Spyker as he stormed into the cell. 'You terrorist bastard!' Thud! Thud! Thud! He kicked Haron's legs, as these were nearest to him. Crash! He jumped on Haron's legs as the little Imam struggled to get up.

'Ooo-eina-a-a God-Allah!' howled Haron.

'Get up! Get up! you nasty thing!' bellowed Spyker as he

123

delivered more kicks to Haron's legs. 'You should respect Major Genis, you pig!' he continued. 'I'll make you respect Major Genis, you dirt!'

Spyker grabbed the now cringing Haron by the lapels and propelled him with all his force across the cell and against the wall.

'I only asked Major Genis for a doctor and for food,' yelped Haron, 'my rib's broken! my stomach's empty! I . . .'

'Doctor? You won't get any doctor! You'll get a coffin to take you out of here!' shrieked Spyker. 'Food? Stomach empty? What do you think this is, a hotel, damn you?'

Spyker was in full cry. He whipped a gun out of his shoulder holster and pressed it to Haron's stomach. He suddenly calmed down and in a low voice hissed, 'If your stomach is empty, how would you like it filled with lead?' he drew back the gun and with a vicious jab drove the point with all his strength into Haron's stomach. Haron crumpled in a heap on the floor, groaning and crying.

'You better see that you talk properly to Major Genis next time,' warned Spyker. 'Do you hear me? Hey! Do you hear me?' he shrieked.

'I'm seeing Major Genis on Monday. I'll talk to him on Monday,' whimpered Haron. 'You come too, you'll see, I'll talk to Major Genis on Monday,' he wailed through his tears.

'Monday, then,' barked Spyker with a self-satisfied smirk, and strutted out of the cell.

Haron's stomach was now in a far worse condition than when it was merely empty! He lay as still as he could and wept and prayed. That evening his food arrived as arranged and as always happened after a visit from Genis. But now he could not eat. But nothing could stop him from praying to Allah for the deliverance of His faithful servant from this hell on Earth. He was beginning to feel that there was only one way out, and that was to die. He did not wish to betray his companions, but he was now wholly uncertain whether he could resist Genis any longer.

Major Genis's plan of campaign had been so well thought out that Haron had even been transferred to a cell reserved for whites for the day, the ostensible reason being that his own cell had to be scrubbed and was therefore wet. This 'white' section could be kept empty for Spyker's part in the operation. Haron was therefore kept in the 'white' cell for the night.

At 8.20 a.m. on Saturday morning the duty constable, Johannes Hendrik Hanekom Burger, assisted him back to his own cell. Haron complained about the pain in his stomach to Burger, and Burger then mocked him with the suggestion that he should see a doctor. But Haron refused. He had now given up hope. A request for a doctor would only mean another visit from the political police, and they were the last people he wanted to see. He wished only to die, but he asked for and was given two pain-killing pills. He would decide in his cell whether it was worth taking them.

Locked up in his own cell again Imam Abdulla Haron felt a gentle breeze of salvation waft through his mind. Allah had answered the prayers of His faithful and steadfast servant. Allah was going to take him away from this hell, from his tormentors, to a place of safety. Death beckoned and he must prepare. He could die with honour; he had remained a member of the faithful all his life; he had met all his obligations to Islam; he had struggled to serve his people and his congregation with all his will and energy; he had kept his word to his comrades – their secret would die with him.

Painfully and methodically the Imam undressed. Next, he should wash himself thoroughly, but there were no facilities. Symbolically he splashed himself with water from his mug. Slowly he donned his pyjamas. He arranged his prayer-mat carefully and, through the blur of pain in his chest, stomach and legs, he knelt in the direction of Mecca and prayed. He prayed for what seemed a long time, and then folded his clothing carefully and put his other things in order. He folded his prayer-mat lovingly and picked up his Koran, kissed it and placed it neatly on the folded prayer-mat. Then he lay down on his blankets, placing a hand upon his stomach inside the cord of his pyjama-trousers on the spot where Spyker had last assaulted him. He rested his head on his other hand and, thus settled and ready to die honourably, murmured a last prayer.

'In the name of Allah, the most gracious, the most merciful, forgive me my sins. Please care for my wife and children. Now more than ever they need your guidance and protection. Oh most merciful one, you are the only one, this I believe. And the prophet Muhammad is your messenger. May peace be on his soul. My wounds are painful and I cannot endure this torture and suffering any longer. Oh merciful one, take my soul; let my tormentors have my body; forgive my weakening. Oh merciful one, let me die now; let my soul be free; let my people be free.'

And then Abdulla Haron was dead.

One hundred and thirty-three days of confinement, abuse, insult, persecution, torture and terror ended for Abdulla Haron on that morning of Saturday, 27 September 1969.

At 10 a.m. that morning, the commander of the Maitland police station, Captain Malan, and the duty sergeant, Petrus Rademeyer, found the dead body of Abdulla Haron while on their tour of inspection of the cells. Immediately a burst of activity swept through the police force. Pienaar, the head of Security Branch was sent for. Photographs of the body were taken in the position in which it was found. The corpse was shipped to the morgue at nearby Salt River. Genis and Spyker had to be found. To them was given the honour of bearing the news to the family. They were in no hurry. It was 8 in the evening before Genis and Spyker visited Galiema Haron and informed her crisply: 'The Imam had a heart attack. He is dead. We are sorry.'

Haron's wife was stunned but, like any Muslim, her first thought was for the body which, according to custom, should be buried as soon as possible. Happy though Genis and his colleagues would have been to have obliged, there were certain formalities which in spite of everything still had to be gone through. They informed her that a post-mortem had to be performed on the corpse and that she could only have the body when this was completed. The body might be available on Monday morning. They left Galiema Haron collapsed on the floor where she had stood.

The news of the death of Imam Abdulla Haron spread like wildfire throughout the country. It was met with mingled horror and disbelief. Visitors offering advice and assistance deluged the Haron house and a private pathologist was hurriedly briefed to represent the family at the post-mortem which was conducted the following day, Sunday, by the senior State Pathologist, Dr Schwar.

Abdulla Haron was buried according to Islamic rites on Monday, 29 September 1969, in the Muslim cemetery on the slopes of Devils Peak Mountain, Cape Town. To accommodate the large crowd of 4000 mourners, the funeral ceremony had to be held in the rugby ground opposite the Haron home. The route taken by the cortège was lined with thousands of people, many of whom joined the procession. By the time the cemetery was reached, a crowd of 30,000 mourners had massed. This vast assembly, gathered to show its esteem for the dead Muslim priest, turned into a spontaneous demonstration against the government and its police force, as speech after speech at the graveside abominated apartheid and its agents.

On 29 September, the day of the funeral, Canon Collins announced in the *Guardian* plans to hold a memorial service at St Paul's Cathedral on Monday, 6 October. 'He is a martyr,' Collins declared, 'a victim of the appalling racial system of South Africa. He was also doing work for the victims of persecution.'

On Thursday, 2 October, the 'Special United Nations Committee on the Policies of Apartheid of the Government of the Republic of South Africa' was convened at the United Nations headquarters. Mr Olajide Alo, the rapporteur from Nigeria, addressed the assembled representatives from fourteen states on the death of Abdulla Haron.

On Monday, 6 October, hundreds gathered in the crypt of St Paul's Cathedral in London to pay homage to the martyr. The gathering consisted of diplomats, representatives of liberation movements from South Africa, and men and women of all races from Britain and abroad. It was the first time in the history of the Cathedral that a service had been held there to commemorate a Muslim. It was the first time ever that a Muslim (Hadji Omar Cassim, an exile from South Africa) had recited verses from the Koran in this great Christian cathedral. The cross and the crescent united in holy condemnation of a system that brutalized men, abused their dignity, battered their minds and killed them.

The gathering was addressed by Canon L. John Collins who spoke of his friendship with Abdulla Haron, the simplicity of the man and his devotion to the cause of the families of victims of persecution. He told the gathering of Haron's courage and his preparedness to die rather than betray those who worked with him.

'This,' the Canon suggested, 'is the type of sacrifice that inspires men and women to continue the noble struggle to rid South Africa of the barbarous system of racial oppression.'

The post-mortem revealed that Abdulla Haron had a certain heart condition and various small and large blood clots (pulmonary embolism and thrombosis in the legs).

The most significant findings were:

(a) 26 bruises ranging from as large as 10 cm × 8 cm to as small as 1 cm × 1 cm;
(b) the 7th right rib was broken;
(c) a haemotoma $2\frac{1}{2}$ cm × $2\frac{1}{2}$ cm near the base of the spine;
(d) at least 10 bruises had been sustained 7 to 10 days before death – most on the right leg;
(e) at least 8 bruises had been sustained 1, 2 or 3 days before death – most on the legs;
(f) the stomach was empty.

Epilogue

It is a peculiarity of the South African police state that, although its practice is patently fascist, formally it hovers in a twilight zone of the 'rule of law', in that some of the régime's activities are still subject to a degree of formal scrutiny by limited judicial process. These formal rights exist because white people exist, and they have been assured that they enjoy 'democratic rights'; although, of course, these liberties are by and large non-existent as far as black citizens are concerned. So far, blacks have not been denied the right of inquiry into the circumstances of death in a police cell. That the results of inquests have often been farcical is, of course, common knowledge.

The inquest into the death of Abdulla Haron was presided over by a magistrate named S. J. Kuhns. Representing the State and the interests of the police was Prosecutor van Graan, and representing the interests of the Haron family were two advocates: 'States Council' Cooper and a junior counsel, Mr B. M. Kies.

Sworn statements were read by various police officers and others and cross-examination was conducted by both the Prosecutor and Mr Cooper. The senior State Pathologist, Dr Schwar, who conducted the post-mortem, stated his findings and was cross-examined. Another medical expert also stated his conclusions on Dr Schwar's findings. The police generally tried to say as little as possible (except where it may have been damaging

129

to the late Abdulla Haron), pleaded 'the security of the State' for not answering some questions, and hid much information from the inquest. A well-orchestrated attempt to hide the fact that Haron was away from Maitland police station for the vital three days, 17 – 19 September 1969, failed. The names of various interrogators were not disclosed, even to the point of avoiding all mention of the predecessor in office of Colonel Pienaar, who took command on 1 August 1969. The police argued that Haron sustained his injuries when slipping and/or falling down a flight of stairs, but this claim was totally disproved by the evidence. However, the evidence failed to move the magistrate. The inquest concluded on 9 March 1970, with a summing up from Prosecutor van Graan and one from State Counsel Cooper.

Van Graan submitted that Haron died of natural causes and that there were no contributory factors. 'The general state of health of the deceased was very low and the likelihood that he died of coronary thrombosis is, in my submission, not improbable.' On the other hand, he argued, if the injuries Haron had sustained did after all contribute to his death and it was accepted that these injuries resulted from his fall down a staircase, nobody could be held responsible. Van Graan further attempted to argue, in the teeth of the expert witnesses and the weight of the evidence, that all of one class of injuries (of a green coloration) could have been sustained in the fall down the stairs.

Apart from suggesting that Haron might have injured himself while alone in his cell, van Graan submitted that the absence of testimony as to how Haron received a second class of injuries precluded any finding of an assault or illegal action by anyone. His most bizarre argument proceeded thus: 'Apparently there are two classes of injuries, the one green and the other red injuries. It is clear from Dr Schwar's evidence that these injuries must have occurred at two stages. Now, assuming that the injuries – the first which were caused by the fall – if all these injuries could contribute to the death, then the Court must still establish which of that class of injuries did contribute to the death. If he fell, and in addition these injuries caused his death, then the other injuries have nothing to do with this case. If the other injuries are the cause of death, as we don't know where they came from, the Court cannot then make a finding. There is no evidence of an assault. That it cannot be explained where the other injuries – the red ones – came from does not mean that they were inflicted in an illegal way or by means of an assault.'

The summing up of States Counsel Cooper (representing the Haron family): Cooper drew the Court's attention to its responsibilities in terms of the law: it had to determine the circumstances and causes of the death and whether any unlawful act or ommission by any person was involved.

Haron was in good health prior to his detention, Cooper pointed out, and had in fact been passed fit for life-insurance purposes only about eighteen months before. But during his detention he had to be seen by doctors on four occasions – 7 and 10 July, and 14 and 15 September.

(The date of 7 July needs revision in view of the fact that Dr Viviers said he placed it at the end of June; and as far as Dr Gosling is concerned, he saw the deceased on 10 July. And, further, he said the deceased told him that he had been seen by a doctor a week earlier. 7 July is a date obtained solely from one of the police witnesses.)

Dr Viviers had not spoken much with the deceased because he was a political prisoner. He found no sign of heart trouble, and prescribed pain-killing pills. He conceded that the chest pains suffered by Haron could have been caused by an assault. On 10 July Dr Gosling found the chest clear but noted tenderness over the ribs. He gave treatment for an 'influenza-like illness' although he was aware that other symptoms were inconsistent with such a diagnosis.

Cooper inferred that Haron had been reluctant to give the police the information they wanted at that time; but suddenly Spyker van Wyk commenced taking a written statement on 2 July which he was able to complete by 11 July. This was a remarkable coincidence. The police concerned have denied that any force was used, but this denial, it is submitted, is patently inconsistent with the evidence as a whole, and should be rejected.

Cooper continued: my submission is that van Wyk's denial [of force] is unacceptable; that even if his denial *is* acceptable, the inescapable inference to be drawn from Haron's failure to complain to van Wyk [about chest pains] is that van Wyk committed, or was a party to, or had knowledge of, an assault which was the cause of Haron's pain . . . the only reasonable inference that can be drawn is that round about this time Haron had been assaulted on one or more occasions.

We go now to the final inquiry. As I indicated during the inquest there seems to be . . . the case seems to fall into two phases. Haron was found dead in the cell at Maitland police station on Saturday, 27 September, at about 10 a.m. He was last seen alive at about 9 a.m. on that day. At 1.30 p.m. on the 28 September, i.e. four months after detention, a post-mortem is held by Dr Schwar who, if I may say, appears to have made a very thorough examination and has given a very comprehensive report.

Now, what did he find? He found widespread bruising, 26 separate bruises, a number of them large, 10×2, 10×9, 10×5, 20×8 cm measuring the larger ones. He finds a haematoma over the lumbosacral area and . . . that the 7th right rib is broken at the costochondral junction. At this stage, as I have suggested, prima facie this is obviously a question of trauma here. As to the exact cause of the trauma, well, that is another inquiry. My submission is that would be the impression and I don't think Dr Schwar, although it is a question of inference, would basically disagree with that proposition.

In addition there were clots in the deep veins of his calves. Now, the immediate inquiry is: how and when Abdulla Haron sustained these injuries. The starting point of this inquiry is that while the Security Police were initially satisfied with the statement which had been reduced to writing between 2 July and 11 July, they thereafter came to believe that it was riddled with lies ['deurspek met leuens']. They made this discovery in September. After the Security had made this discovery they decided to endeavour to obtain from Haron a satisfactory statement, which they intended to reduce to writing. That statement was never obtained from Haron.

It is 7.42 a.m. and now we come to the critical period. At 7.42 a.m. on the Wednesday morning, on 17 September, Haron is taken by Major Genis from the Maitland police station to Caledon Square. The previous and only other occasion he had been removed from Maitland police station by the Security Police and as far as we know by any other police, was on 21

August. This is clear from the evidence of Captain Malan who testified late during the morning on the last occasion.

According to Captain Malan, Major Genis returned Haron to Maitland police station at 9.40 on Friday the 19th. In other words, he was away two nights and three days. Now, the fact that Haron had been away from Maitland police station for three days and two nights only came to light after Captain Malan had been requested, through the Court, to ascertain when Haron had been removed from the Maitland police station by the Security Police. Both Major Genis – with respect, I submit – and van Wyk concealed from the Court the fact that he had been taken away for three days and two nights from the Maitland police station. And as this was only the second occasion that he had been removed it is inconceivable that they should have forgotten about it. Major Genis was questioned on this, and he said that he couldn't remember, he would go back and check up and possibly find out.

My submission is that if we take the circumstances as a whole, the concealment of this fact becomes a sinister one. Now, between 12 July and 17 September, Haron was seen on two occasions by Dr Gosling i.e. on the 14th and 15th and, as we know, that had to do with piles. At that stage, on the face of it Haron appeared to be in good health. On the morning of the 17th we know that the magistrate saw Haron and that Lieutenant Colonel Pienaar saw him either after the magistrate or on the same morning. Lieutenant Colonel Pienaar questioned Haron about certain aspects of his written statement.

It is not quite clear, not even today, after the evidence, particularly after Sergeant van Wyk's evidence of this morning, as to what transpired on 17 September, what transpired on 18 September and what really transpired on 19 September. Initially, Major Genis claimed that he could not remember. Be that as it may, the truth of the matter is that a blanket had been drawn over the 17th to the 19th. What we do know is that at approximately 4 p.m. on Friday, 19 September, Haron was seen by Major Genis and van Wyk. And on their way out, they saw that Haron fell on the steps. It was after this absence from Maitland police station, Cooper emphasized, that Haron's pattern of ill-health and suffering suggested that he had been severely injured. Amazingly although District Surgeons were

133

available none was called at any stage until after his death – and that was to certify that he was dead. During the whole weekend, there is no satisfactory explanation placed before this Court as to why he did not receive medical attention, whereas he had previously received it.

Here again is an odd, a strange feature: whereas Geldenhuys had gone to Dr Viviers to get pain pills on Monday, the 22nd, Genis apparently, according to his evidence, contacted the Maitland police station also for pain-killing pills. There was a great deal of activity about it, in the police ranks, about this man's state of health, and again one asks: if there was all this activity, why wasn't a doctor called? As he is given pain-killing tablets, this man is obviously complaining.

When we link this with the post-mortem findings of the widespread bruising over his whole body which, with respect, must have occurred before the 20th, then the explanation stands out. In addition to that, we have the evidence of Sergeant Rademeyer and Constable Burger that whereas at the beginning of his detention at Maitland police station Haron walked about during his exercise, he wasn't unduly energetic admittedly to the extent of doing physical jerks, press-ups, etc., but during the latter part of September he did not even walk any more, but merely stood around in the sun. On occasion, according to Constable Burger, Haron did not even leave his cell. With respect, this is a picture of a sick man, and it follows after the episode of the 17th to the 19th, because apparently it is one continuous course of conduct. On the day of his death when Constable Burger saw Haron, between 8.20 a.m. and 9 a.m., he merely stood in front of his cell door and did not move about during his exercise period. He then complained of a stomach ache and asked for pain pills. He was given some pills.

There is some bleeding we find at the post-mortem and the bruising to the centre of the stomach, isn't that giving him a painful stomach? Isn't that the most apparent explanation for this man's discomfort at this stage? With respect, our submission is that the medical evidence, the bruising, the haematoma and the broken rib would have had the following effect upon the deceased: he would have felt considerable pain, movement would have been painful, he would have tended to immobilize himself and one would have expected him to complain.

The medical evidence also infers that the injuries were caused by trauma, i.e. force applied to the person of the deceased. Now, in contrast to this picture of pain and suffering which presents a typical pattern of post-trauma, is the evidence of Major Genis and Sergeant van Wyk.

Major Genis says on the mornings of 22 and 24 September he saw Haron for a few minutes in his cell at Maitland police station. On 22 September, Major Genis had visited Haron specifically to find out whether he had any complaint. At about midday on 26 September, accompanied by Sergeant van Wyk, he again briefly saw Haron at Maitland police station. On all these occasions Haron had no complaint except that he asked for pain pills for a headache on the 22nd or 24th. On 26 September he appeared completely normal and happy, according to the evidence of Major Genis. This is the man of whom we have got a picture as a sick man suffering pain, and this witness says that he appeared normal and healthy.

Sergeant van Wyk alleges that when he accompanied Major Genis he saw Haron in his cell at the Maitland police station on the 26th, Haron was quite cheerful. ['Heeltemal opgewek' (completely cheerful)], and he had no complaint.

Now there is this fundamental difference between the picture of the period of 20 – 27 September, presented by the Police at the Maitland police station and Captain Geldenhuys which is consistent with the medical evidence of pain resulting in im-mobility, which would have been following the infliction of trauma, revealed by the post-mortem examination; and the picture of cheerful good health drawn by Major Genis and Sergeant van Wyk. It is submitted that the former is the true picture, and that the evidence of Major Genis and Sergeant van Wyk in this connection cannot be believed, more particularly as, according to Captain Geldenhuys, Haron specifically asked for Major Genis on 20 September. Haron must have complained to Major Genis at least but, if Major Genis and Sergeant van Wyk are to be believed, that he did not complain, then this is only explicable on the basis that Major Genis and Sergeant van Wyk had either assaulted him, or had been party to an assault, or had knowledge of an assault that had been committed upon him.

And, sir, may I say – with respect – it is not without signific-ance that Major Genis visited him twice during the week ending

135

September 27; and may I add to this that it is not without significance that a District Surgeon wasn't called in during that period either. According to Major Genis, he visited Haron to find out how he was. Why was he so interested to know how he was?

These are all small factors that fall into place and are explicable only on one basis: from the nature and extent of Haron's injuries, that Major Genis and van Wyk had to resort to this to obtain satisfactory statements. The false evidence given by both Major Genis and van Wyk regarding the state of health of Haron after the 19th, *that the Security Police had resorted to violence to obtain a statement from Haron*, and the absence of a satisfactory explanation from the Security Police to account for those injuries, my submission is that the only reasonable inference to be drawn is that after he had seen the magistrate on 17 September, and during the period 17 – 19, while he was in the exclusive custody of the Security Police, Abdulla Haron sustained these injuries as a result of an assault on him.

Cooper ridiculed the explanations for Haron's injuries which had been offered by Genis and van Wyk, observing pointedly that the alleged fall down the stairs came to light only after they had seen the corpse in the mortuary. He then showed that there were crucial contradictions between this explanation and the affidavits they had submitted to the Court. Moreover, in the course of their testimony they also shifted their emphasis under cross-examination in order to attempt to validate their offered explanation.

Major Genis gives us the evidence which shows a very superficial fall. He again says that the deceased must have slipped down on his bottom. Your Worship, I ask you in this particular case to view this explanation with a great deal of scepticism. *The man who could give you explanation as to how he sustained the injuries is dead, he cannot talk for himself.* The people, in whose custody he was, had every reason to give an explanation to cover up, if in fact they were responsible for his injuries. After all, one wouldn't expect a burglar, who is taken back to the house which he had broken into, to detect the person who has entered there.

These men, these members of the Security Police who were in

136

charge, are the ones who are under suspicion, and if this were a normal criminal trial, the Court would view an explanation, the easiest thing in the world to put up, with a great deal of care, before being satisfied that it is possibly true. But if you analyse . . . first of all, it doesn't account for all the bruises. Dr Schwar made it perfectly clear. He said there were certain bruises that were older than others. So there were bruises inflicted at different times. Secondly, in so far as the green bruising is concerned, it is perfectly clear and it must be immediately conceded that individual bruises can be explained. Obviously they can be explained. It wasn't terribly difficult to precisely predict exactly the movement of the body moving down the staircase, but it is the cumulative effect of those bruises to which regard must be paid, and where the witness says that the man came down on his seat and he has the impression that the man isn't seriously injured, not injured at all, because they asked him immediately: 'How do you feel?' and he said he was all right, 'ek het my net vaal gestkrik' [I went grey with fright]; then, with respect, the whole basis falls away and then if you test the mechanics of the situation you have got here bruises front, back and on the sides. Does he turn round like a top to come sliding down the stairs, to account for all these bruises? And that is not what they said he did when he came down. I know my learned friend put to Sergeant van Wyk this morning that he can't remember now, it was dark. That wasn't Sergeant van Wyk's original explanation. He didn't seek refuge in darkness and say: 'Well, I just cannot tell you how this man fell, all I know is I heard a thud and the next thing I saw him on the ground.' Sergeant van Wyk at all material times, until this morning, tried to give an explanation. As I see it, it is a contradictory explanation, an unacceptable explanation. But giving him the benefit of the doubt, explanation for the trauma which was sustained by the deceased.

The question then is a question of inference. It is not suggested that Haron inflicted these injuries on himself. It is not suggested that unauthorized persons gained access to his cell at Maitland. The inference, therefore, draws on, it was either a fall (and I am not going to make the ordinary corny crack 'or he was pushed'), or he sustained the injuries as the result of assault. And I have already intimated the factors which I submit might, if taken cumulatively, point to one thing only: *this man was beaten for the purpose of extracting a statement from him.* That is what happened between the 17th and the 19th.

That trauma now starts playing a vital role; as a result of it he is immobile in his cell. Little did these people know, the people who were responsible, that in fact at that time *the man had a diseased coronary artery.* But it is quite clear that the immobilization had set in. It gave rise to, or let's put it this way, it aggravated a clotting process that was going on in his veins, in the veins of the calf. And that clotting process gave rise to a pulmonary embolus. The doctor found a pulmonary embolus. It also resulted in possibly affecting the circulation, the sluggishness of the blood. *It triggered off this myocardial attack*, i.e. *the severe sudden restriction of blood to the heart which caused the death of the deceased.*

You therefore, with respect, if you get down to the reality of the situation, take the picture as a whole, cast aside hypothetical situations, have a clear picture of why this man died. *He died as a result of a heart attack which was triggered off by trauma. By a trauma occurring to him during the period 17 – 19 September*. My submission is, the Court should have no difficulty in so finding. My submission is, therefore, that the finding of the Court should be accordingly.

In so far as the Court is concerned, in so far as the identity of the persons who are responsible for this trauma are concerned, it is for the Court to decide on the evidence before it whether it can identify these persons. If it cannot identify these persons then it can only say that they were persons whose identity is to the Court unknown, they might have been in the employ of the Security Police. Those are my submissions, Your Worship.

Judgement of Magistrate Kuhn: Findings in terms of section 16 of the Act:
  (a) Identity of the deceased person, *Abdulla Haron*, Malay male, about 45 years of age, shopkeeper.
  (b) Date of death, 27 September 1969.
  (c) Cause or likely cause of death: Myocardial Ischaemia: a likely contributing cause being a disturbance of the blood-clotting mechanism and blood circulation due to, in part,

trauma superimposed on a severe narrowing of a coronary artery.

(d) Whether the death was brought about by any act or omission involving or amounting to an offence on the part of any person: a substantial part of the said trauma was caused by an accidental fall down a flight of stone stairs. On the available evidence, I am unable to determine how the balance thereof was caused.

State pays damages: On 18 May 1971, a mere ten days short of two years from the date of the arrest of Abdulla Haron, it was publicly announced by the Minister of Police that an 'ex gratia' payment of R5000 was being made to Mrs Galiema Haron in settlement of a claim for damages of R22,125 brought by her against the Ministers of Police and Justice for the ill-treatment and/or neglect of her husband while in the exclusive custody of the police. Mrs Haron accepted the payment and withdrew her damages claim.

The Latin words 'ex gratia' mean 'as an act of grace'. This is an act of which, the authors believe, the present South African régime is incapable.

Diagram of Haron's injuries revealed at the inquest

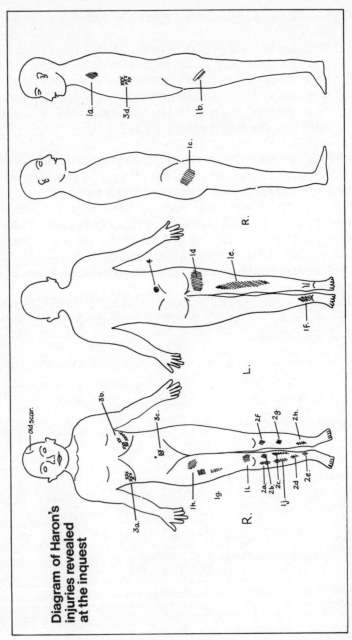

old scar.

Appendix

Dr T. G. Schwar's recorded notes after examining the body.

Most Distinctive Autopsy Findings:
1. Coronary arteriosclerosis
2. Pulmonary embolism
3. Subpleural 'petechiale' bleedings
4. Bruises on legs and chest.
Body was chilled.
Rigor mortis was present in arms and legs.
Post-mortem discoloration was spread over back and the right lateral side of the body.

A. The following visible bruises were observed:
1. *With a green-yellow appearance:*
a. on the lateral part of the left upper-arm 2 cm × 1 cm.
b. over the lateral part of the left upper-leg 10 cm × 2 cm.
c. over the right hip area 10 cm × 9 cm.
d. on the posterior-superior part of the right upper-leg 10 cm × 5 cm.
e. over the posterior portion of the right knee 20 cm × 8 cm.
f. above the left heel 5 cm × 2 cm.
g. spread over the anterior of the right upper-leg 2 cm × 2 cm, 8 cm × 3 cm.
h. anterior on the right upper-leg, two parallel running bruises, 7 cm long and total width $2\frac{1}{2}$ cm.

i. above the medial portion of the right knee 7 cm × 7 cm.

j. over the medial portion of the right lower-leg + in the centre 10 cm × 8 cm.

2. *With a red appearance:*

Spread over the anterior and antero-medial part of the right lower-leg:

    a. 3 cm × 2 cm.

    b. 4 cm × 1½ cm.

    c. 8 cm × 2 cm.

    d. 1 cm × 1 cm.

    e. 2 cm × 1½ cm.

Spread over the anterior antero-medial part of the left lower-leg:

    f. 2 cm × 2 cm.

    g. 1 cm × 1 cm.

    h. 3 cm × 3 cm.

Dissection of some [enkele] of the injuries described under 1 and 2 show bruises limited to the sub-skin tissue.

B. Injuries observed on dissection:

3. *Bruises of the sub-skin tissue:*

    a. over the lateral inferior part of the right chest 6 cm × 8 cm with a yellow-brown colouring.

    b. as a. but of the left chest 1½ cm × 1½ cm, 6 cm × 1 cm, 3 cm × 3 cm.

    c. in the wall of the abdomen 1½ cm × 1½ cm.

    d. of the lateral, inferior portion of the left chest 4 cm × 4 cm.

In the sub-pleural area of the left chest under the bruises there is a thin blecan spread over an area of ± 8 cm cut through [drursuit]. The right 7th rib is broken at its costo-chondral [costo chondrale] junction.

4. Haemotomia [haematoom] ± 2½ cm cut through [drursuit] over the lumbosacral area.

C. Other observations:

5. Clots [stolsels] in the deep veins [venas] of the calves, more or less in the middle of the [laar] leg, less to the left, more to the right.

INDEX

146